BIOMES
OF THE WORLD

VOLUME 2

Deserts

MICHAEL ALLABY

GROLIER
EDUCATIONAL

About This Set

Biomes of the World is a nine-volume set that describes all the major landscapes (biomes) that are found across the Earth. Biomes are large areas of the world where living conditions for plants and animals are broadly similar, so that the vegetation in these locations appears much the same. Each of the books in this set describes one or more of the main biomes: Volume 1: The Polar Regions (tundra, ice cap, and permanent ice); **Volume 2: Deserts** (desert and semidesert); Volume 3: Oceans (oceans and islands); Volume 4: Wetlands (lakes, rivers, marshes, and estuaries); Volume 5: Mountains (mountain and highland); Volume 6: Temperate Forests (boreal coniferous forest or taiga, coastal coniferous forest, broad-leaf and mixed forest, Mediterranean forest and scrub); Volume 7: Tropical Forests (rain forest and monsoon forest); Volume 8: Temperate Grasslands (prairie, steppe, and pampas); Volume 9: Tropical Grasslands (savanna).

The books each have three sections. The first describes the geographical location of the biome, its climate, and other physical features that make it the way it is. The second section describes the plants and animals that inhabit the biome and the ways in which they react to each other. The final section of each book deals with the threats to the biome and what is being done to reduce these. An introduction in Volume 1 includes a map showing all the biomes described in this set, and a map showing all the countries of the world.

Throughout the pages of this set there are diagrams explaining the processes described in the text, artwork depictions of animals and plants, diagrams showing ecosystems, and tables. The many color photographs bring each biome to life. At the end of each book there is a glossary explaining the meaning of technical words used, a list of other sources of reference (books and websites), followed by an index to all the volumes in the set.

Published 1999 by Grolier Educational, Danbury, CT 06816

This edition published exclusively for the school and library market

Planned and produced by Andromeda Oxford Limited, 11–13 The Vineyard, Abingdon, Oxon OX14 3PX, UK

Project Manager: *Graham Bateman*
Editors: *Jo Newson, Penelope Isaac*
Art Editor and Designer: *Steve McCurdy*
Cartography: *Richard Watts, Tim Williams*
Editorial Assistant: *Marian Dreier*
Picture Manager: *Claire Turner*
Production: *Nicolette Colborne*

Origination by Expo Holdings Sdn Bhd, Malaysia
Printed in Hong Kong

Set ISBN 0-7172-9341-6
Volume 2 ISBN 0-7172-9343-2

Biomes of the world.
        p.   cm.
    Includes indexes.
        Contents: v. 1. Polar regions -- v. 2. Deserts -- v. 3. Oceans -- v. 4. Wetlands -- v. 5. Mountains -- v. 6. Temperate forests -- v. 7. Tropical forests -- v. 8. Temperate grassland -- v. 9. Tropical grassland.
        Summary: In nine volumes, explores each of the earth's major ecological regions, defining important features, animals, and environmental issues.
        ISBN 0-7172-9341-6 (hardcover : set : alk. paper). -- ISBN 0-7172-9343-2 (hardcover : vol. 2 : alk. paper)
        1. Biotic communities--juvenile literature. 2. Life zones--Juvenile literature. 3. Ecology--Juvenile literature. [1. Biotic communities.] I. Grolier Educational (Firm)
QH541.14.B57   1999
577--dc21   98-37524
                                                    CIP
                                                    AC

Contents

The Physical World of Deserts

*T*he image of a desert is distinctive. An ocean of sand stretches as far as the eye can see, the sun beats down mercilessly, and there are no clouds; it is a dry, inhospitable, and often beautiful environment. But the deserts of the world also present dramatic contrasts of landscape and weather—and most are not sandy.

Deserts are typically empty, barren places (the word comes from the Latin *deserere*, meaning "to abandon") that are characterized above all by their dryness. A desert will form if the rate at which water evaporates is greater than the rate of precipitation (rain, snow, fog, or dew). As it seldom rains in arid areas, this is measured as the amount of water that will evaporate during a stated period from an open water surface. This is called the potential evaporation and is compared with the precipitation over the same period. The higher the temperature, the greater the potential evaporation will be. But regardless of the temperature, a desert is likely to form if the average amount of precipitation is less than 10 inches (250 mm) a year.

Although deserts are often associated with shimmering heat, they are not all hot. Deserts form even in the polar regions (see Volume 1), but for this to happen the precipitation must be much lower than that which would produce a desert in a hot climate.

The Gobi, the Takla Makan, and the Turkestan Deserts in central Asia, and the desert complex in western North America, are all cold deserts. These deserts experience moderately high temperatures in summer, but in winter temperatures fall to well below freezing.

In some parts of the world all or nearly all the rain falls during one season of the year, and conditions are dry the rest of the year. This produces a semiarid environment.

Hot and cold deserts cover more than one-quarter of the Earth's land surface and represent some of the most extreme environments in the

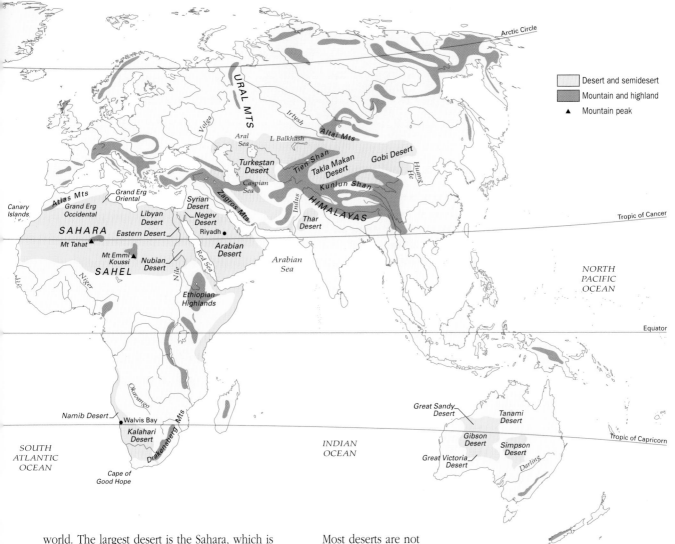

Desert and semidesert

Mountain and highland

▲ Mountain peak

world. The largest desert is the Sahara, which is about the size of the United States and stretches across North Africa, joining the Arabian Desert. The American deserts include the Colorado Desert and the Mojave Desert with its Death Valley—one of the hottest places on Earth. The Atacama Desert in northern Chile is one of the driest deserts in the world.

Much of the central part of Australia is desert and includes the Great Sandy Desert, the Gibson Desert, and the Great Victoria Desert. In southern Africa there are the Namib and the Kalahari Deserts; the latter is known for its hunter inhabitants, the Kalahari Bushmen.

Most deserts are not sandy. More often, the desert surface consists of stones, small rocks, or gravel. Deserts may also consist of salt pans, formed by lakes or rivers that no longer exist, or large areas of dried mud flats.

Deserts are often thought of as flat and low-lying. This is not entirely true. There are two mountain ranges in the middle of the Sahara, for example, with high peaks. Mount Tahat, in Algeria, is 9,574 feet (2,918 m) high, and the peak of Mount Emi Koussi, in Chad, is even higher, at 11,205 feet (3,415 m). The western side of the Arabian Desert is mountainous, rising in

DESERTS OF THE WORLD. Many deserts lie in or close to the tropics. Among the exceptions are the Gobi and Takla Makan Deserts in central Asia. These deserts are arid because they are situated so far away from the oceans that they do not encounter rain-bearing clouds. Mountain ranges are included on the map for context.

Cell 3

Cell 2

Cell 1

THE THREE-CELL MODEL OF ATMOSPHERIC CIRCULATION. Warm air at the equator rises, flows away, and descends in the tropics. Some of it flows back toward the equator; the remainder flows away from the equator. Over the poles descending air flows away. In the middle latitudes air flowing away from the poles meets air flowing toward the poles, and the air rises. This circulation is driven by convection—the displacement of warm air by cooler, denser air. The patterns it forms are called convection cells. There are three sets of convection cells, and this description is called the three-cell model. The circulation produces the major wind belts of the world.

places to more than 6,500 feet (2,000 m). There is high ground in the Mojave Desert, and the Atacama Desert running parallel to the Pacific coast lies among the foothills of the Andes.

It is in the semiarid regions around deserts that people can live. The Sahel, bordering the southern Sahara, is a typical semiarid region, and its climate supports enough vegetation to provide pasture for livestock. However, a severe drought began there in the late 1960s, reached its climax in about 1972 and 1973, and did not end until the 1980s. During this time the Sahel was desert. Rainfall is erratic in these regions, but unlike the true desert, they recover when the rains eventually return.

WHY DESERTS ARE DRY

As the map (pages 4 and 5) shows, most of the world's major deserts are in or close to the tropics—the region close to the Tropic of Cancer (latitude 23° 30' N) and the Tropic of Capricorn (23° 30' S).

Tropical Deserts and Trade Winds

The reason for this was discovered almost by accident. Sailors knew that the winds blowing westward toward the equator—from the northeast in the Northern Hemisphere and the southeast in the Southern Hemisphere—were very constant, and they relied on them for westward ocean crossings. They called them the trade winds. (The word *trade* used to mean "track," and "to blow trade" means to blow steadily in one direction.) No one knew why these winds were so steady.

The first person to attempt an explanation was the astronomer Edmund Halley (1656–1742). He suggested that air is heated more strongly at the equator than elsewhere. The warmed air rises, and its place is taken by air flowing in from the north and south.

Some years later, the meteorologist George Hadley (1685–1768) suggested that the rotation of the Earth swings the winds so that they flow from an easterly direction. In fact, it is the tendency of moving air to turn on its own axis that causes the swing. This was not discovered until 1856, by the American meteorologist William Ferrel (1817–1891).

Hadley believed warm air rises at the equator, flows all the way to the poles, then sinks and flows back to the equator. Scientists now know that it is rather more complicated. Warm air rises at the equator, but it descends again in the tropics. This is not quite what Hadley proposed, but this circulation is nevertheless called a Hadley cell.

The warmer the air is, the more water vapor it can hold. Air rising at the equator is very warm

MAJOR DESERTS OF THE WORLD

Area	square miles	sq. km
North America		
Mojave	15,000	38,8500
South America		
Patagonian	260,000	680,000
Atacama	140,000	363,000
Africa		
Sahara	3,500,000	9,100,000
Kalahari	275,000	712,250
Namib	97,000	251,000
Middle East		
Arabian	1,600,000	3,000,000
Syrian	200,000	518,000
Asia		
Turkestan	750,000	1,900,000
Gobi	374,420	970,000
Thar	231,600	600,000
Iranian	150,000	390,000
Takla Makan	115,000	297,000
Australia		
Australian	979,700	2,538,000

A VIEW FROM SPACE of the Namib Desert, which extends for 1,200 miles (1,930 km) along the Atlantic coast of Namibia. What look like ripples are huge sand dunes, with rocky hills projecting through them.

and carries a great deal of water vapor, most of it evaporated from the ocean. Higher levels in the atmosphere have lower pressure, and as air rises to these levels, it expands and cools. This causes most of the water vapor to condense into droplets. These form clouds, and the water falls as rain. The region around the equatorial belt has a wet climate.

High above the equator the air that has risen and is flowing away from the equator is very cold. Because it is so cold, it is also very dry. Some distance from the equator it meets warmer air. This is less dense than the cold air, so the cold air descends below it and continues sinking until it reaches the ground. Just as rising air gets cooler, descending air gets warmer. The air that sinks to the ground in the tropics is warm, but it is still very dry, and that is why tropical climates are dry. Most of the air flows back toward the equator, forming the trade winds, and some flows away from the equator.

Descending air produces high pressure at the surface. Air flows outward from areas of high pressure, and this contributes to the aridity of desert climates.

Polar and Middle Latitude Deserts

Polar deserts form for a similar reason. There, the surface air pressure is high. Air is subsiding and spilling out at the surface, away from the Pole. Polar air is very cold and dry, and its outward movement prevents warmer, more moist air from bringing precipitation into very high latitudes.

There are also dry climates in middle latitudes, far from either the tropics or the polar regions. Near the center of a large continent the

air is dry because of its distance from the ocean. Air reaching the continental interior must travel a long distance over land, where it has ample opportunity to lose moisture and little chance of gathering more from evaporation at the surface.

The Rain-Shadow Effect

Mountain ranges can also produce deserts. Air is forced to rise as it crosses the mountains. Air pressure decreases with height above sea level, so as air rises, it enters a region of lower pressure and expands. As it expands, it also cools because its molecules lose energy as they move farther apart.

Warm air can hold more water vapor than cold air, so as the air cools, some of its water vapor condenses, just as moisture vapor in your warm breath condenses into a cloud on a cold day. Clouds on the mountains often produce rain or snow, or fog that wets everything it touches. By the time it has crossed the mountains, the air may be fairly dry.

On the far side of the mountain—the "lee" side—the air may start to sink. Now the reverse happens. As the air enters a lower region, with higher pressure, it is compressed. Compression means its molecules move closer together, and they gain energy. This warms the air, and because it is warmer, it can hold more water vapor. There is less condensation, and the air is dry. The lee side of the mountains can lie in a "rain shadow."

Except for the South American coastal strip, most of the Atacama Desert is in the rain shadow of the Andes. The desert areas of California are also in the rain shadow of the coastal range of mountains.

A SANDSTORM consists of sand lifted and carried as a dense, swirling cloud by winds of more than 30 mph (48 km/h). This storm is approaching a village in Mauritania, on the southern edge of the Sahara.

MAJOR DESERTS OF THE WORLD *(right)*. **The map includes the semiarid regions, and the winds that blow across them in January and July.**

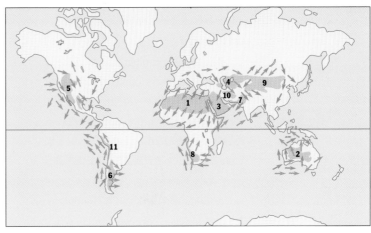

Desert and semidesert
→ January winds
→ July winds

1 Sahara
2 Australian
3 Arabian and Syrian
4 Turkestan
5 North American
6 Patagonian
7 Thar
8 Kalahari and Namib
9 Gobi and Takla Makan
10 Iranian
11 Atacama

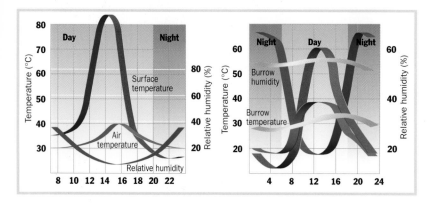

Conditions fluctuate widely in the desert but remain much more constant below ground. This fact is exploited by desert animals that burrow. The graph on the left above shows the surface temperature (red), air temperature (blue), and relative humidity (green) in Sudan during a 24-hour cycle. The graph on the right above compares these with the temperature and humidity inside the burrow of a fat sand rat (Psammomys obesus), a type of gerbil, over 24 hours.

WINDS AND STORMS

The dry winds blowing out of the deserts often have local names. Those blowing from the Sahara toward the West African coast are called harmattan, and the hot southerly wind blowing across Egypt is called khamsin. Winds that cross the Mediterranean from the Sahara are called sirocco in Italy and leveche in Spain.

Dry air moves outward, but it is supplied from above—no moist air flows inward to replace it. On the eastern coasts of continents, however, the trade winds blow onshore, bringing moisture. Consequently, tropical deserts are rather less common on the eastern side of continents.

The weather is often violent in the deserts. During the day the ground is heated strongly, and the sand surface quite commonly reaches 180°F (85°C). Convection cells develop as air rises and is replaced by inflowing air near ground level. Occasionally, the rising air will carry some water vapor. As this condenses, huge clouds form, and there can be torrential rain. Iquique, in Chile, once went for 14 years without rain, but it has also received 4 inches (100 mm) in a single day.

More usually, though, the convection produces no cloud or rain, only wind. At other times, strong winds are caused by low-pressure weather systems crossing the desert. In both cases the wind may lift and carry sand. A 12-mph (19-km/h) wind will raise medium-sized, dry sand grains (about 0.001 inches—0.25 mm—in diameter), and as its speed increases, so does the size of the grains the wind will lift.

Consequently, desert surfaces are covered either with sand dunes or with stones—the wind sweeps away all the smaller particles, and dunes form where the sand grains finally settle. In sandy deserts strong winds can bring sandstorms lasting several days. In March 1998 a khamsin wind caused a sandstorm that swept across Egypt and on into Jordan.

Dust Devils

Where a small area is heated more strongly than its surroundings, air rises by convection. Air spirals inward at the surface to replace it and is drawn upward in its turn, carrying with it the dust and sand it has raised. This is a dust devil. It resembles a tornado, but there is no water vapor to condense in it, no cloud above it. It begins at ground level and grows upward, unlike a tornado, which descends from the base of its cloud. Dust devils can be tall, occasionally reaching more than 6,500 feet (2,000 m). Although they are less violent than tornadoes, they can demolish flimsy buildings.

Dust devils are very common, and several different types exist. They last no more than a few minutes, but as one sinks to the ground and

vanishes, another rises to take its place. These are the "whirlwinds" described in the Old Testament, where they are likened to armies wreaking havoc on everything in their path.

REFLECTING AND ABSORBING HEAT

Light colors reflect the light. The light reflected from white surfaces, such as snowfields and cloud tops, can be dazzling. Dark colors absorb light. Radiant heat and light are both forms of electromagnetic radiation; they differ only in their wavelengths. Surfaces that reflect or absorb light also reflect and absorb heat, and this applies to the surface of the Earth just as much as to light-colored clothing that keeps us cool in summer.

Albedo

The reflectivity of a surface is measured as its albedo. This is the percentage of the total amount of radiation striking the surface that is reflected. It can be written either as the percentage—65 percent, for example—or as a decimal (0.65).

Albedo varies widely from one surface to another. A coniferous forest, for example, has an albedo of 5–15 (or 0.05–0.15), depending on the particular type of trees. A desert is much lighter.

A SALT PAN in the Namib Desert. Occasional rains cause rivers to flow, then run dry. Their water dissolves chemical salts from the underlying rocks. As the water evaporates, the salts are left behind, gradually accumulating at the surface. Eventually, they can reach concentrations high enough to poison vegetation. Here, trees have been poisoned by the accumulated salts that form the surface.

On average, deserts have an albedo of 25–30; the albedo of dry sand (remember, not all deserts are sandy) is higher—35–45. What is not reflected is absorbed, so while the forest reflects less than 15 percent of heat, it absorbs a much higher proportion of the available solar energy than a desert does.

Below the surface of the tree tops the forest is proportionately warmer than the desert (but it is not actually warmer, because deserts are in lower latitudes). This affects the climate of the desert by limiting the warming of the ground.

Where the albedo is higher, the temperature below ground level is lower. Because sand is more reflective than the average desert surface, conditions below ground there are cooler. Cloud reflects a great deal of light and heat (albedo of up to 90 percent), which is why it feels cooler beneath a cloudy sky than when the sky is clear.

Radiated Heat

As soon as an object has absorbed heat, making it warmer than its surroundings, it starts radiating it. During the day the ground absorbs heat faster than it can radiate it, so it grows warmer. At night, however, it absorbs no heat but continues radiating its own heat, so it grows cooler.

Air is warmed by contact with the ground, so during the day the ground heats the air and at night it cools it. This happens everywhere, but in hot deserts the effect is most extreme. As the graph (see page 10) shows, the temperature at the surface of a sandy desert can vary by about 80°F (45°C) between midday and midnight.

Above the surface of the ground the temperature decreases very rapidly with height. At midday, the top of a camel's hump, about 8 feet (2.4 m) above the surface, may be in air that is 60°F (33°C) cooler than the sand on which the animal is standing. Below ground the fall in temperature is even more dramatic. When the sand surface is at 140°F (60°C), 5 feet (1.5 m) lower down the temperature may be a comfortable 60°F (15.5°C).

The desert surface warms quickly in the morning and cools just as quickly in the evening. This is because of the intensity of the solar heat beating down on it, of course, but that is not the whole explanation. The Sun shines just as strongly on the ocean, but it warms and cools much more slowly. The difference in the way a substance, such as rock, sand, or water, responds to heat is called the specific heat capacity of that substance.

This is calculated as the amount of heat energy, in joules (1J = 0.239 calorie), required to raise the temperature of 1 kg (1 kg = 2.2 lb) of the substance by 1 K (1 K = 1°C = 1.8°F). The specific heat capacity of sand is 0.8, and that of most rocks is between about 0.7 and 0.9. Sea water has a specific heat capacity of 3.93; fresh water of 4.18. This means that almost five times more heat is required to raise the temperature of sea water by one degree than to warm sand by the same amount. Consequently, the desert heats and cools much faster than the sea.

THE DESERT LANDSCAPE

Rocks expand when they are heated by the Sun and contract again as they cool. But they do not expand and contract evenly because they are not heated evenly. The upper surface, directly

DESERT LANDFORMS. The features of deserts are sculpted by wind, sand, and water. Wind-blown deposits form dunes, the best-known type of which is the barchan, a crescent-shaped dune. Oases form when a depression in the desert reaches down as far as the water table.

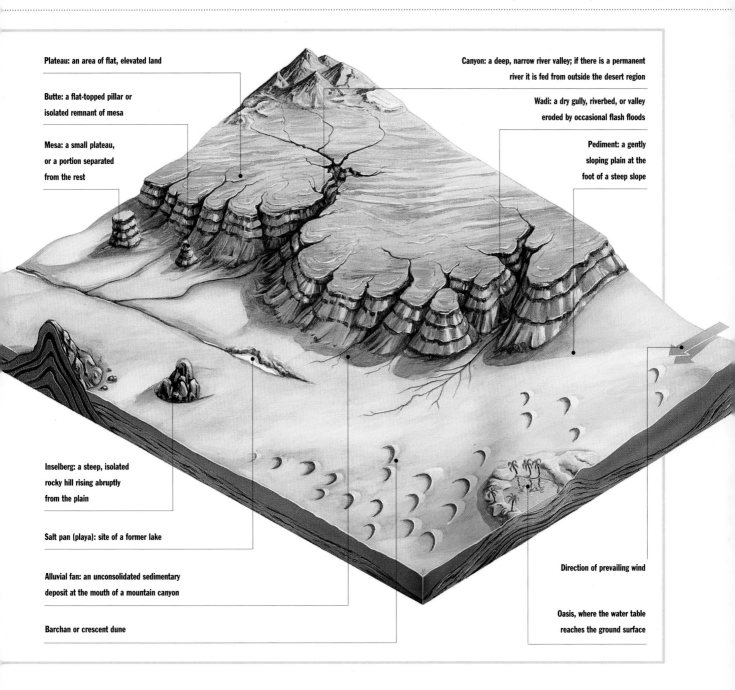

Plateau: an area of flat, elevated land

Butte: a flat-topped pillar or isolated remnant of mesa

Mesa: a small plateau, or a portion separated from the rest

Canyon: a deep, narrow river valley; if there is a permanent river it is fed from outside the desert region

Wadi: a dry gully, riverbed, or valley eroded by occasional flash floods

Pediment: a gently sloping plain at the foot of a steep slope

Inselberg: a steep, isolated rocky hill rising abruptly from the plain

Salt pan (playa): site of a former lake

Alluvial fan: an unconsolidated sedimentary deposit at the mouth of a mountain canyon

Barchan or crescent dune

Direction of prevailing wind

Oasis, where the water table reaches the ground surface

exposed to the Sun, becomes much hotter than the underside, and the outside of the rock becomes hotter than the interior. In time, this expansion and contraction cracks the rock. Then particles begin to break away from it. The scouring action of the incessant wind detaches grains to form sand, then blasts that sand against the solid rocks. Some rocks resist this attack better than others. Over millions of years heating, cooling, and erosion by the wind combine to shape the land surface.

In some deserts, especially in North America, there are hills made from sedimentary rocks in which the layers (strata) lie more or less

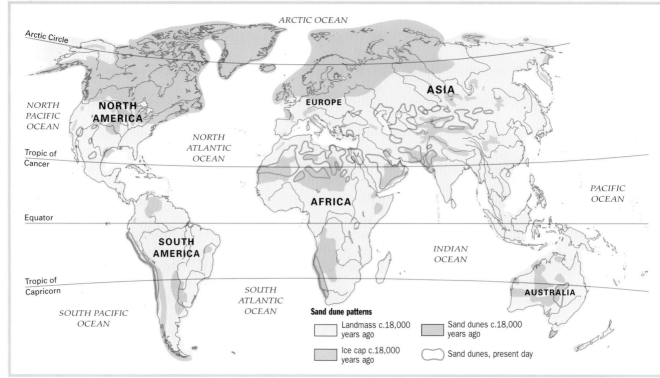

ARCTIC OCEAN

Arctic Circle

NORTH
PACIFIC
OCEAN

NORTH
AMERICA

EUROPE

ASIA

NORTH
ATLANTIC
OCEAN

Tropic of
Cancer

PACIFIC
OCEAN

AFRICA

Equator

SOUTH
AMERICA

INDIAN
OCEAN

Tropic of
Capricorn

SOUTH
ATLANTIC
OCEAN

AUSTRALIA

SOUTH PACIFIC
OCEAN

Sand dune patterns

Landmass c.18,000
years ago

Sand dunes c.18,000
years ago

Ice cap c.18,000
years ago

Sand dunes, present day

horizontally. These are sometimes flattened as layers of softer surface rock are loosened, then swept away. What remains is a plateau, made from more erosion-resistant rocks and standing above the desert floor.

An individual hill may be left with a flattened top. This is called a mesa. Little by little, a mesa can be worn away until it is reduced to a flat-topped pillar, called a butte. A larger isolated hill, made from hard rock and rising from the plain, is called an inselberg.

Dried-up river channels cross the plateau and extend into the plain. Small, shallow valleys are called arroyos in the United States and wadis (or ouadis) in Arabic-speaking countries. Other channels form steep-sided canyons. Rain is rare, but it can be extremely heavy, and then the rivers become torrential, savagely eroding their beds. This occurs over very long periods.

Sometimes evidence of this erosion can be seen. At the foot of the steep cliff forming the edge of the plateau the ground may slope fairly gently down to the plain. The shallow slope, or pediment, is made from material eroded from the plateau above. Elsewhere, fast-flowing rivers have deposited particles and stones washed

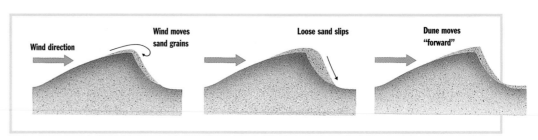

Wind direction

Wind moves
sand grains

Loose sand slips

Dune moves
"forward"

ADVANCING DUNES. Sand dunes advance as grains are blown forward and loose sand falls down the face of the dune.

RETREATING DUNES.
About 18,000 years
ago, when the ice
sheets of the last ice
age reached their
greatest extent and
thickness, desert
sand dunes covered
a much larger area
than they do today.

where the river emerges from highlands and meets the plain, and the slope of its bed becomes shallower. A fan-shaped zone of deposit made by a former river is called an alluvial fan.

Where it is covered with small stones or gravel, the surface is called desert pavement or reg. The stones are often rounded from having been constantly rolled against one another.

Polish and Varnish

In some places the stones are polished by the constant movement of wind-blown sand, so they appear smooth and shiny.

In other areas various chemical reactions result in a polishing effect. These produce a shiny coating known as desert varnish. The coating, less than 0.04 inches (1 mm) thick, is made from iron and manganese oxides and clays. This ranges in color from orange, where iron predominates, to black, where the surface is rich in manganese. Scientists are not sure how it forms, but probably it is a result of the oxidation of substances deposited by the wind. (Oxidation is a chemical reaction in which a substance combines with oxygen.) Chemical reactions in the surface layers of the rock itself also produce orange, red, or yellow deposits—called a weathering rind—but this penetrates much deeper into the rock.

Salt Deserts

When the rain falls, the water dissolves mineral salts from the underlying rock. The salts are washed away, but the river runs dry. Water remaining in the ground is drawn to the surface, where it evaporates. The salts dissolved in the water do not evaporate, however. (If you leave a dish of saltwater in the sun, the salt will be left behind when the water evaporates—this was a traditional way of obtaining salt.) Gradually, a layer of "evaporite" salt deposits accumulates until it forms a salt pan (or playa)—a flat, sometimes broad, expanse of dry salt.

Near salt pans and coasts evaporation leaves behind minerals that crystallize into flowerlike shapes. The minerals that most commonly crystallize in this way are barite (barium sulfate) and gypsum (calcium sulfate), and the "flower" this produces is called a desert rose or rock rose.

SAND DESERTS

Sand covers no more than about 30 percent of the Arabian Desert and 11 percent of the Sahara. It is less common in North American deserts, covering only about 2 percent of the total area.

During the ice ages temperatures were low throughout most of the world. Water evaporated less readily, so the air was drier. Fewer clouds formed, and there was less rain and snow. In these conditions the deserts expanded.

When the last ice age (called the Devensian in Britain and Wisconsinian in North America) reached its climax, about 18,000 years ago, deserts covered much larger areas than they do today. Sand dunes leave traces geologists can recognize. The sand probably accounted for no bigger a proportion of their total area than it does today.

In the northern Sahara, however, there are basins filled with fine sand deposited by rivers that flowed long ago, when the climate was wetter. This sand formed dunes; the highest, called draas, are nearly 1,000 feet (300 m) high. Some of the dunes have settled so firmly that they no longer move.

Some deserts consist of great "sand-seas," known as erg or areg (from the Arabic *irj*). The largest are the Grand Erg Occidental in Algeria and Grand Erg Oriental across the border between Algeria and Tunisia. These are some of the most dramatic parts of the Sahara. The Erg Iguidi, Erg Chech, and Erg Edeyen are also in Algeria. The Libyan Desert is also mainly sand.

Shifting Sand

Sand carried by the wind eventually falls to the ground. Because winds in any particular place blow more often from one direction than from any other, sand is shifted mainly in one direction, and it tends to fall in the same area. Loose, dry sand flows much like a liquid, and the wind forms shapes in it that resemble waves.

Loose sand grains lying on the surface are rolled forward by the wind. The wind piles on more and more grains, but because it blows from just one direction, the grains form a heap with a shallow slope on the side facing the wind (the windward side) and a much steeper slope on the sheltered (leeward) side. The leeward slope grows steeper as more and more sand is blown up the windward side, until the slope is too steep to be stable. Grains of sand start to roll down it from the top, only to be replaced by more grains pushed up the shallow slope. Little by little, the entire dune (and, because the dune is not alone, the entire system of dunes) moves forward in the direction of the prevailing wind.

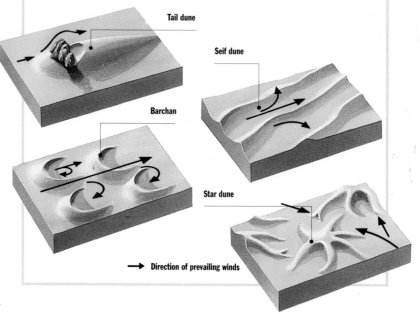

SAND DUNE TYPES. The shape of sand dunes is affected by wind direction, seasonal variation, vegetation cover, and the shape of the ground. Barchans are perhaps the best-known dunes. Seifs (from the Arabic word for sand) are also known as linear or longitudinal dunes, and their ridges can be more than 330 feet (100 m) high. They can form from barchans if there is a seasonal shift in wind direction.

Tail dune

Seif dune

Barchan

Star dune

→ Direction of prevailing winds

This process is not confined to deserts. It happens wherever there is a large amount of sand, most commonly along coasts. Extensive dune systems often form behind sandy beaches, and although dunes are smaller than desert dunes, they move in just the same way, and for the same reason.

Coastal dunes are often stabilized by planting grasses that produce underground stems (rhizomes), which bind sand grains together. Similarly, vegetation can stabilize desert dunes.

Dune Shapes

If there is abundant sand and the wind blows from only one direction, dunes form like ocean

SHIFTING SAND DUNES in the Namib Desert in southwestern Africa. The dunes are stabilized where plants have managed to establish themselves. The plants find water below ground and from the coastal fogs that frequently envelop the Namib.

waves, one behind another in straight lines at right angles to the wind. These are called transverse dunes.

Where the wind direction varies by a few degrees, the straight lines of transverse dunes cannot form. Instead, the approximately straight lines run down wind. These are called longitudinal, linear, or seif dunes.

If there is insufficient sand to form transverse dunes, a steady wind produces crescent-shaped dunes, with the tails of the crescents pointing down wind. These are called barchan dunes. As more and more sand accumulates, the ends of the barchans link, forming a series of long, wavy dunes called barchanoid ridges.

A dune may also form in the lee of a large rock or other obstacle. Wind blows sand over the obstacle and drops it on the far side. This produces a tail dune, pointing down wind.

When the wind direction is variable, star dunes form, with a mound at the center from which curved "arms" radiate.

WEATHERING AND DESERT SOIL

The action of heat, cold, wind, and water together break up rock into fine particles. Below ground chemical compounds dissolve as they come into contact with water. They move in the soil solution and react with other compounds

they encounter at the surface of rock particles. These physical and chemical processes are known as weathering, and they mark the beginning of the conversion of rock into a soil that will sustain plants.

Living organisms contribute greatly to weathering. Many bacteria can extract the substances they need from rock. They form colonies, and the wastes they produce provide food for other organisms. Lichens appear: collaborations between fungi and either algae or cyanobacteria (bacteria that contain a blue pigment, also known as blue-green algae). The fungus obtains mineral substances from the rock.

Their wastes, and their remains when they die, allow mosses to grow, and eventually small herbs and grasses appear. As the development continues, a layer of organic material accumulates on the surface. Meanwhile, below ground, chemical weathering continues.

Eluviation

Rain falling on the surface drains downward. As it does so, it dissolves compounds from the upper layers and washes them to a deeper level —this is called eluviation. Gradually, the character of the ground changes. Organic matter —leaves, twigs, animal droppings—lie on the ground. Just below the surface mineral particles become mixed with organic matter, and the organic matter decomposes. Eluviation moves chemical compounds from this layer to the one below, and below that chemical weathering continues. Distinct layers are formed, and what started as a purely mineral material has now become soil.

IRRIGATION near Riyadh, Saudi Arabia. Where water deep below the ground is tapped, small areas of desert can be irrigated and crops can be grown. The rotating sprinkler arm produces circular "fields." But the scarcity of water means that the scope of irrigation projects such as this is limited.

These layers are called horizons. A
fully developed, fertile soil in temperate
regions will have several of these layers.
A trench with vertical sides cut into the
ground will expose the horizons as a soil
profile. Soil scientists classify soils and
give them names. Most desert soils are called
Aridisols (the name means "dry soil"). This is the
most abundant type of soil in the world,
covering about one-fifth of the total land area.

Pedogenesis

Soil formation—known as pedogenesis—can
occur only where two conditions are satisfied.
Temperatures must be high enough for plants to
grow, which means they must be higher than

about 40°F (5°C) for at least several months in
the year, and there must be a supply of water.
The chemical reactions that produce weathering
involve compounds dissolved in water. Eluviation
requires water. All living organisms require at
least a little water, and without plants and
animals, as well as the fungi, bacteria, and other
microscopic organisms that live in the soil, there
is no organic material to decompose.

Tropical deserts are warm enough, but the
scarcity of plants means that there is little organic
matter. The lack of water means that the
chemical reactions that weather the soil into
nutrients—soluble compounds plant roots can
absorb—proceed very slowly. When there is rain,
it is often so heavy that it washes away soluble
nutrients. The wind also affects the way the soil
develops, by blowing away surface particles and
depositing them elsewhere.

Beneath the dust and sand many desert soils
are rich in clay that has been washed into them
from elsewhere some time in the distant past.
This indicates that many regions that are now
desert once had a much wetter climate. This
certainly applies to much of the Sahara, and it is
also true of the Mojave Desert, where the soil is
a mixture of sand, clay, and loam.

The desert climate makes soil development
slow, but desert soils can be made to grow
crops, and in many countries they are.
Cultivation is possible because many of the
modern soils have not always been as they are
today. Once they were fertile, but deteriorated
when the climate changed, so their development
has been arrested. With irrigation and careful
cultivation many desert soils can be returned to
their former condition.

The Natural World of Deserts

*D*eserts are harsh places, but they are far from lifeless. In some the ground is quite densely covered with plants that are adapted to the dry conditions. Other deserts "bloom" whenever it rains, with plants that can flower and set seed before the water evaporates. Wherever there are plants, there are animals to eat them. And wherever there are animals that graze, there are other animals that hunt them.

Ecology is the scientific study of communities of living organisms together with their physical and chemical environments. A living community and its environment that can be studied as a unit distinguishable from other units adjacent to it is called an ecosystem. A clearly definable area, such as a pond, forest, field, or desert, can be studied as an ecosystem; ecologists trace the relationships among its components and the movement of energy through it.

Plants produce sugars through photosynthesis—the formation of organic compounds using water, carbon dioxide, and light energy. Because green plants can make their own food from simple chemical substances, they are called primary producers. They form the basis of every ecosystem.

In a desert plants can grow only where the sand is no longer shifting, and even among stable dunes they are scarce. Seeds that germinate in shifting sand are soon buried, and the young plants killed.

Animals cannot manufacture food for themselves the way plants can. Ecologists call them consumers because the only way they can obtain food is by eating the producers.

In the desert consumers include herbivores (such as rodents and gazelles), which are animals that feed upon the plants. Because there are so few plants, the bigger herbivores must travel to find enough food for their needs, often covering considerable distances.

Carnivores (such as cats, dogs, foxes, snakes, and eagles) feed on other animals. They are also consumers, but because they feed on herbivorous consumers, they are called secondary consumers. The distinction is not as sharp as it seems, because many animals eat both plant and animal foods, so they are both primary and secondary consumers.

Not all the consumers are as big as gazelles or eagles, nor even the size of mice. Insects such as ants, bees, grasshoppers, and locusts feed on the plants, and wasps, spiders, and scorpions hunt them.

The desert soil has no covering of fallen leaves or other plant material, but plants do shed leaves, even in the desert. This, and the organic remains of dead plants and animals, provides food for another group of organisms, the decomposers. Beetles bury organic material and consume it below ground. In addition to the beetles and their young, or larvae, there are mites and still smaller animals, along with fungi and bacteria, all finding food among the organic litter lying on the ground. The decomposers are

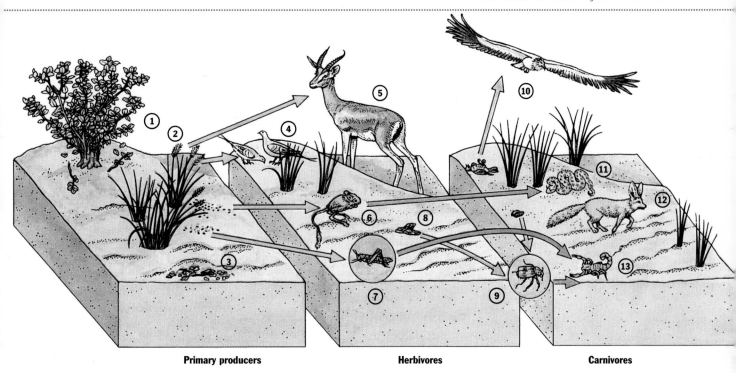

Primary producers   **Herbivores**   **Carnivores**

in turn hunted by animals such as centipedes and spiders, and their wastes, too, are eaten.

Much animal life in deserts is hidden. A beetle may scurry past, or a scorpion may suddenly rush from its lair to seize a grasshopper, but generally there is little to see. In the middle of the day, when the heat is intense, some animals bury themselves in the sand, waiting for evening before they venture out to search for food.

DESERT PLANT SURVIVAL

During the long wait between rains desert plants must somehow stay alive. Plants must cope not only with drought, but also with the extreme heat, which can kill them. Between freezing and about 95°F (35°C) the rate of photosynthesis in a green plant doubles with every 18°F (10°C) rise in temperature. Between 77°F (25°C) and 95°F, however, the doubling is sustained for only a

few minutes, after which the photosynthetic rate falls back to its previous level. Above 95°F, the rate decreases rapidly, and at temperatures above 113°F (45°C) most plants die quite quickly. In Death Valley, California, one of the hottest desert areas, average daytime temperatures in the hottest month, July, reach 166°F (47°C).

Some plants, especially trees and shrubs, have adapted to the dryness by having long roots that seek water far below ground. They may also have a shallow system of lateral roots, which can absorb water as soon as the ground becomes moist.

Other plants survive by allowing their leaves, stems, and roots to die away, so all that remains are their seeds or bulbs. The seeds have tough, protective coats, and those of some species can be dormant (alive but in a resting torpid condition) but remain viable (capable of germinating) for several years.

The ocotillo (*Fouquieria splendens*), found in the North American deserts, dries out and

Energy flow

⟹ Primary producer/
   primary consumer
➡ Primary/secondary
   consumer
⟹ Dead material and
   detritus/consumer

Components of the ecosystem

1 Sodom apple plant
2 Desert grass
3 Seeds and detritus
4 Spotted sandgrouse
5 Dorcas gazelle
6 Desert jerboa
7 Desert locust
8 Feces
9 Dung beetle
10 Egyptian vulture
11 Horned viper
12 Fennec fox
13 Scorpion

A DESERT ECOSYSTEM. Desert animals adapt to limited resources by adopting nomadic feeding patterns. There is little material to decompose.

loses its leaves. The creosote bush (*Larrea divaricata*), also common in the North American deserts, also survives in this way. Its leaves turn brown and are shed, and its leaf buds shrivel. Inside the buds, however, the young leaves are dormant. As soon as moisture comes into contact with the plant, the buds open, and the "dead" plant recovers.

Germination

Most plant seeds germinate when the soil around them warms up in spring. The seeds of desert plants respond not to warmth, however, but to moisture. There is a danger in this. A brief, isolated shower might be enough to wet the soil around seeds, but by the time they germinate, there may be no water for the young plants.

Desert plants have adapted to this. Many seeds will respond only if more than half an inch (13 mm) of rain has fallen in a short time, dissolving chemical substances in the seed coats that inhibit germination. Others must stay wet long enough for bacteria on their coats to release chemicals that trigger germination.

There are other ways to avoid the dangers of premature germination. *Cassia obtusifolia*, a legume (member of the pea family), has seeds of different types. Some germinate as soon as they are moistened. If more rain falls, the young plants are ready for it. Other seeds must be thoroughly soaked before they will germinate. If the shower is not followed by more rain, the first plants will be lost, but the others will not. *Neurada procumbens*, a plant growing from the deserts in the Middle East to the Thar Desert of northwestern India, has seeds that germinate one at a time, each time it rains.

Some plants retain the parts growing above ground, with the seeds held on the flower stalks. As the plant dries, these stalks bend and lower until they touch the ground. When the rain moistens them, they straighten up, and the seeds are washed out. This is the strategy used by *Plantago cretica*, a Middle Eastern member of the plantain family, and by *Gymnarrhena micrantha*, a plant found in the Negev Desert in southern Israel. Its seeds have hairs and are dispersed by the wind.

When plants germinate, they must do so quickly. By the time the ground has dried again, the plants must have produced leaves and flowers. The female flowers must have been pollinated, fruits and seeds must have been formed, and the seeds stored. A plant that completes its life cycle within a few days is called an ephemeral.

There are desert species of *Convolvulus*, related to bindweed, that complete their life cycles, from germination to seed, in three to six weeks. Some desert ephemerals do so in as little as two weeks. The pillow cushion plant (*Fredolia aretioides*) of the Algerian Sahara produces roots and begins photosynthesis within 10 hours of its seeds being wetted. Seeds of *Blepharis ciliaris*, a plant of African and Middle Eastern deserts, are ejected from their capsule explosively as soon as the plant is wetted, and they germinate within an hour.

Plants that appear and disappear so fast have no time to grow large. Most desert ephemerals are pollinated by insects, and because all of them germinate and grow at the same time, competition for the attention of insects is keen. To attract pollinators, the plants

DESERT PLANTS survive long periods of drought and use brief periods of rain. The illustrations show a scene in the Sonoran Desert, Arizona, and the response of plants there to rain. After a long dry period *(top)* the cacti appear healthy, but the woody plants have no leaves and look dead. Following a brief but heavy shower *(bottom)* there is water, but it will not be available for long. The cacti have flowered, and the prickly pear (*Opuntia* species), in the right foreground, is greener than it was. The woody plants have produced leaves, the yucca (*Agave* species), behind the prickly pear, has flowered, and herbs have appeared and are also in flower.

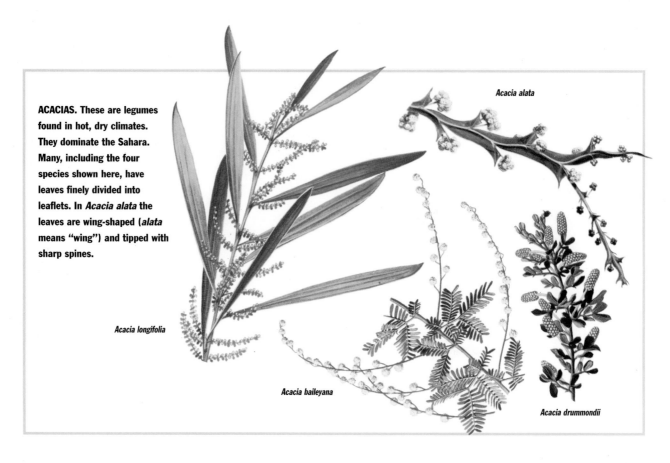

ACACIAS. These are legumes
found in hot, dry climates.
They dominate the Sahara.
Many, including the four
species shown here, have
leaves finely divided into
leaflets. In *Acacia alata* the
leaves are wing-shaped (*alata*
means "wing") and tipped with
sharp spines.

Acacia alata

Acacia longifolia

Acacia baileyana

Acacia drummondii

produce masses of brightly colored flowers. This
causes the desert to "bloom" very soon after rain
has fallen.

REDUCING WATER LOSS

Plants absorb water through their roots,
transporting it to their living cells. They lose
water by transpiration, through small pores in
their leaves called stomata (through which gases
are also exchanged). Transpiration helps to cool
the plant, but the loss of water clearly presents a
problem in arid conditions. Many desert plants
deal with this by keeping their stomata closed
during the hottest part of the day, when the rate
of evaporation is highest.

In some plants a thick, waxy cuticle (or
skin) also reduces water loss. Holly (*Ilex
aquifolium*) and the holm (or holly) oak
(*Quercus ilex*) have leaves of this type, although
they cannot tolerate an extremely dry climate.

Many desert plants have very small leaves,
usually with the stomata on the underside, which
reduces their surface area and, consequently,
water loss. Leaves may even be reduced to
needles, as in coniferous trees and shrubs such
as pines (*Pinus* species), cedars (*Cedrus* species),
and junipers (*Juniperus* species), which grow in
the North African and Middle Eastern deserts.
Toughening leaves has the added advantage of
making them less palatable to animals, and
thorns add further protection—as in the acacias
of African and Australian deserts.

Cacti

Members of the cactus family (Cactaceae), which grow in the deserts of North and South America, usually have no leaves, but bear sharp spines. These are easily detached, so any animal so much as brushing against the plant collects dozens of tiny needles that pierce the skin painfully and are extremely difficult to remove. The spines, and also the branches and flowers, grow from cushionlike pads set in rounded, raised areas called areoles.

One of the best-known cacti is the saguaro, or giant cactus (*Carnegiea gigantea*), which grows in the southwestern United States and in northern Mexico. This is the tallest of all cacti, growing to 65 feet (20 m), weighing more than 12 tons, and having a lifespan of about 200 years. Its spines grow on ridges. Another well-known cactus, the prickly pear (*Opuntia* species), has no true leaves and a flattened, swollen stem that grows in short, jointed sections, and it is covered with spines. The plants can be the size of small trees or grow low to the ground.

With leaves reduced to needles, the cacti use their young stems for photosynthesis. The stems are green, but turn gray or brown with age. In some treelike cacti the older stems become woody and lose their spines. The stems have a cylindrical structure and woody inner tissues, like a skeleton of hollow bones.

Some cacti, and the ice plant (*Mesembryanthemum crystallinum*), found in southern Africa, are

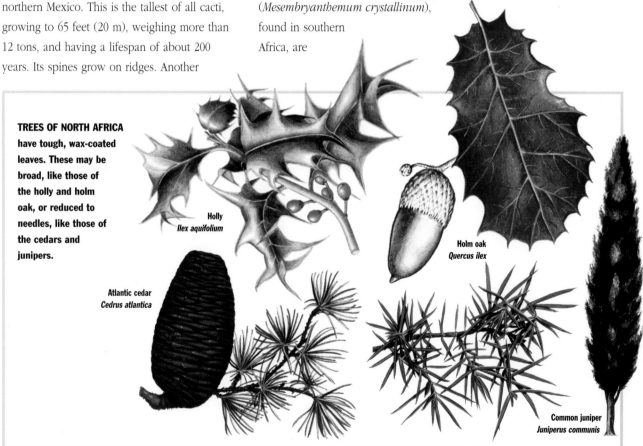

TREES OF NORTH AFRICA have tough, wax-coated leaves. These may be broad, like those of the holly and holm oak, or reduced to needles, like those of the cedars and junipers.

Holly
Ilex aquifolium

Holm oak
Quercus ilex

Atlantic cedar
Cedrus atlantica

Common juniper
Juniperus communis

covered in tiny, shiny silvery hairs. These reflect sunlight and trap a layer of air next to their cuticles, reducing evaporation.

In some plants, including cacti, the stems themselves store water. This is for their own use during the dry season, and it is unpalatable or poisonous to many grazing herbivores. Plants that can store water in their tissues are known as succulents.

In the deserts of Africa and India the local equivalent of the cactus is the Euphorbiaceae, the family of the euphorbias, or spurges. Not all euphorbias are succulents, or desert plants—the rubber tree and cassava plant belong to this family—but some are remarkably similar to cacti. *Euphorbia stapfii*, for example, looks much like a small version of the saguaro cactus. Succulent euphorbias store water in their stems and are usually poisonous to many animals. Some species growing in seasonal climates produce leaves in the rainy season, but many euphorbias, like cacti, use their stems for photosynthesis.

Living Stones

Among the most unusual plants of the desert are the so-called living stones. Like cacti, they are succulents—they store water. But they also avoid being eaten by herbivores by being well camouflaged amid the stones where they grow; they are undistinguishable from them, except when they are in flower. Their flowers, like those of other desert plants, are bright and eye-catching.

The living stones comprise 37 species in the genus *Lithops*. They originally grew in southern Africa, although they are now widely cultivated as ornamental plants.

OASIS PLANTS: THE DATE PALM

There are places in most deserts, but especially in the Sahara, where a natural depression in the rocks lowers the ground surface enough to bring underground water within the reach of plant roots. This can form an oasis.

Of the many different plants that grow around oases, the date palm (*Phoenix dactylifera*) is most characteristic. The date palm tree grows up to 80 feet (24 m) tall and has been cultivated since at least 3000 B.C. They are now grown from Morocco to India and in some of the drier areas of the United States, such as Arizona and California. The dates are the fruit. Yellow when they are ripe (but brown when dried), they form in huge bunches hanging from the crown.

A sugary sap is also obtained from the crown of the tree. This can be boiled to produce sugar, or fermented to make an alcoholic drink called toddy or palm wine.

There are several types of date. The most popular soft-date variety, Deglet Noor, are often sold in boxes with the fruits attached to their stems. Dry dates are an important food among desert peoples. They can be stored for a long time and ground into a type of flour.

ADAPTING PHOTOSYNTHESIS

Water loss through transpiration is a serious problem for plants in hot deserts. Photosynthesis requires that the stomata be open to allow the

Saguaro
Carnegiea gigantea

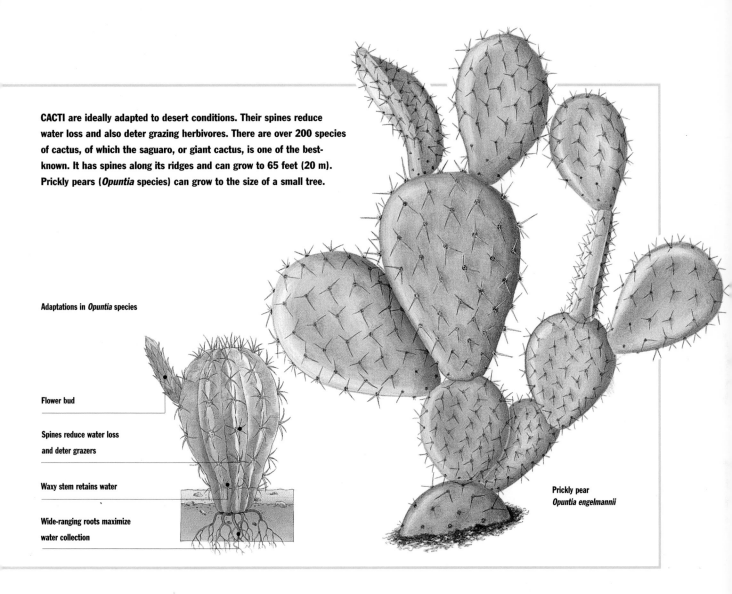

CACTI are ideally adapted to desert conditions. Their spines reduce water loss and also deter grazing herbivores. There are over 200 species of cactus, of which the saguaro, or giant cactus, is one of the best-known. It has spines along its ridges and can grow to 65 feet (20 m). Prickly pears (*Opuntia* species) can grow to the size of a small tree.

Adaptations in *Opuntia* species

Flower bud

Spines reduce water loss and deter grazers

Waxy stem retains water

Wide-ranging roots maximize water collection

Prickly pear
Opuntia engelmannii

exchange of gases, but this also allows water to leave the plant. Some plants have adapted to arid conditions by modifying this process.

Photosynthesis uses carbon dioxide and water, and it produces glucose, oxygen, and water. Critical to the process is light energy from the Sun and chlorophyll, the green pigment in plants. The process is represented in the following equation:

$$6CO_2 \text{ (carbon dioxide)} + 12H_2O \text{ (water)} + \text{light energy}$$
$$\rightarrow C_6H_{12}O_6 \text{ (glucose)} + 6O_2 \text{ (oxygen)} + 6H_2O \text{ (water)}$$

The reactions proceed in two stages. The first stage is a photochemical, or "light" stage. This is where chlorophyll absorbs light energy, converting it into chemical energy and storing it, in a process called photophosphorylation. Also, during this stage water is split into hydrogen, which is stored, and oxygen, which is released.

The second stage is sometimes called the "dark" stage, as it is not dependent on light (although it takes place in daylight). In this stage carbon dioxide is incorporated into the plant cells. Then, in a series of reactions using energy stored in the first stage, carbon dioxide is used to synthesize glucose. The reactions are controlled by enzymes—substances that must be present for a reaction to take place, but that are not altered by that reaction.

The entire series of reactions was discovered by the American biochemist Melvin Calvin and is known as the Calvin cycle.

C3 and C4 plants

The first compound in the Calvin cycle is called 3-phosphoglycerate, the "3" referring to the three carbon atoms it contains. Plants using it are called C3 plants. These include most plants of temperate and cold climates. The enzyme at the start of the cycle can accept either oxygen or carbon dioxide. During the daylight, when photosynthesis reduces the amount of carbon dioxide in the cells, it accepts oxygen, forming a product that splits in two, and sends some carbon out of the cycle. This is called photorespiration, and it wastes carbon.

Some plants, including sugarcane and corn (maize), that occur in hot climates where sunlight is very intense have evolved a different series of reactions. They are called C4 plants because their first compound—oxaloacetate—has four carbon atoms. Almost no photorespiration occurs in C4 plants. They use carbon very efficiently, which means that they do not need to keep their stomata open for as long as C3 plants to synthesize the same amount of glucose.

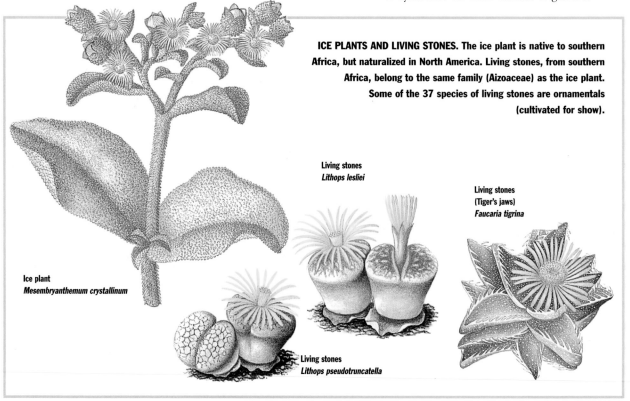

ICE PLANTS AND LIVING STONES. The ice plant is native to southern Africa, but naturalized in North America. Living stones, from southern Africa, belong to the same family (Aizoaceae) as the ice plant. Some of the 37 species of living stones are ornamentals (cultivated for show).

Living stones
Lithops lesliei

Living stones
(Tiger's jaws)
Faucaria tigrina

Ice plant
Mesembryanthemum crystallinum

Living stones
Lithops pseudotruncatella

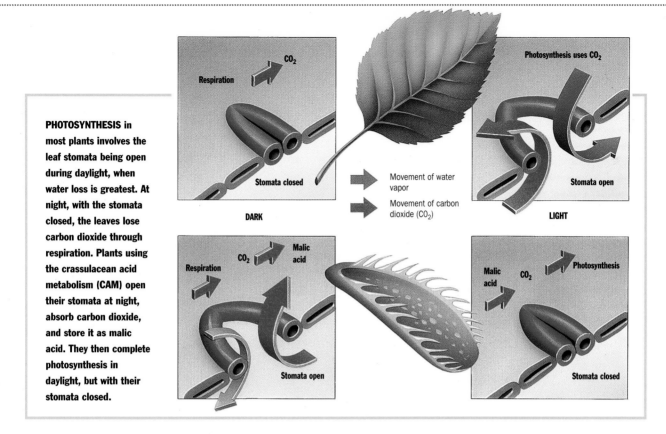

PHOTOSYNTHESIS in most plants involves the leaf stomata being open during daylight, when water loss is greatest. At night, with the stomata closed, the leaves lose carbon dioxide through respiration. Plants using the crassulacean acid metabolism (CAM) open their stomata at night, absorb carbon dioxide, and store it as malic acid. They then complete photosynthesis in daylight, but with their stomata closed.

CAM

These plants must open their stomata during the day, however, so they can lose water. Succulents of desert climates, including the ice plant and living stones, many cacti (but not euphorbias), and other species, have evolved a third type of photosynthesis. This was first discovered in members of the family Crassulaceae, comprising succulent herbs and shrubs, and it is called the crassulacean acid metabolism, or CAM.

At night, when it is cool and most plants have their stomata closed, CAM plants open their stomata. Carbon dioxide enters their cells and is incorporated into several organic acids (hence the "acid" in the name), in which form it is stored until morning. Then the stomata close, and photosynthesis begins, by reactions similar to those of C4 plants, with the stored carbon dioxide being released as it is required.

CAM plants therefore synthesize carbohydrates like other plants, but they lose no water during the day.

USING THE FOGS

Discovered in 1860 by Dr. Friedrich Welwitsch, a German botanist, the welwitschia (*Welwitschia mirabilis*) is one of the world's strangest plants, which derives moisture from fog.

The plant produces winged seeds that germinate in wet years, producing two embryonic leaves (cotyledons) that photosynthesize for about 18 months before true leaves appear. The plant grows only two leaves, from a short stem, but these leaves grow about 5 inches (13 cm) a year and continue to do so throughout the life of the plant. It can live for

**Components of the
ecosystem**

1 Welwitschia
2 Short grasses
3 Seeds
4 Darkling beetles
5 Ant
6 Gerbil
7 Namib clown dune cricket
8 Sidewinder snake
9 Barn owl
10 Sand lizard
11 Spotted eagle owl

500 or more years. The leaves wear away at their tips, forming a huge mass of vegetation.

The welwitschia grows in the Namib Desert on the coast of South Africa. One of the driest deserts, despite bordering the South Atlantic, this desert is also home of the living stones. Just offshore the cold Benguela current flows northward. Air is chilled as it crosses the cold water, producing low cloud that often drifts inland at night, sometimes bringing fog. The cloud and fog keep temperatures fairly low—the average annual temperature in the Namib Desert is 62°F (17°C)—and penetrate up to 15 miles (25 km) inland. The coastal town of Walvis Bay has an average of 55 foggy days a year.

Plants such as the welwitschia and the living stones derive a significant proportion of their moisture from these fogs, some absorbing it directly through their leaves.

Beetles in the Fog

Animals also exploit the fogs. Perhaps the most unusual are some species of darkling beetles (family Tenebrionidae), also found in the Namib Desert. They have long legs,

so their bodies are held well clear of the hot ground. They gather along ridges facing the sea, and as the fog rolls in, they raise themselves on their front legs, so they look as though they are standing on their heads. Water droplets collect on their wing cases (elytra), then trickle down to their mouths.

ANIMAL ADAPTATIONS

Desert survival requires the ability to shelter from or endure the intense heat and, if necessary, to go for long periods without drinking. Many mammals achieve this.

Small mammals of the desert include rodents, gerbils, and mice. Larger ones include antelopes, gazelles, and camels—the most famous desert inhabitants. Some species of wallabies and kangaroos are found in the Australian deserts. These animals are marsupials (pouched mammals).

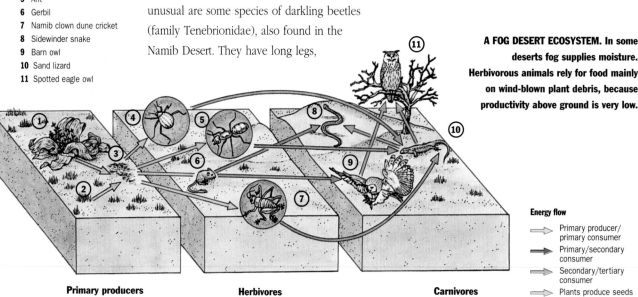

**A FOG DESERT ECOSYSTEM. In some
deserts fog supplies moisture.
Herbivorous animals rely for food mainly
on wind-blown plant debris, because
productivity above ground is very low.**

Primary producers   **Herbivores**   **Carnivores**

Energy flow

⇒ Primary producer/
    primary consumer
⇒ Primary/secondary
    consumer
⇒ Secondary/tertiary
    consumer
⇒ Plants produce seeds

Large animals cannot bury themselves to shelter from the heat, although species such as the hill kangaroo or wallaroo (*Marcopus robustus*) spend the day in caves or other shelters where the humidity is relatively high. In the absence of burrowing, animals must find other ways of keeping cool, and some are particularly ingenious. Some kangaroos, for example, cool themselves by salivating profusely, then licking their tails, bellies, and feet.

Large mammals enjoy some advantages, however. They can cover much greater distances in search of food and drink than, say, small rodents. Also, larger animals have a smaller surface area in relation to their volume than do small animals. This means that a big animal absorbs heat more slowly than a small one, and it takes longer for its temperature to rise.

All animals lose water in their urine. They must urinate to eliminate metabolic wastes that would otherwise be harmful. Desert-dwelling mammals excrete highly concentrated urine and very dry feces, having reabsorbed as much water as possible from these wastes. Some can then lose water equal to up to 20 percent of their body weight with no ill effect.

Drinking only occasionally, or not at all, brings another advantage: security. Water holes are few and far between and are attractive to predators, as they, too, can drink should the wait for prey make them thirsty.

When desert mammals do find water, they can drink very fast; some can restore the water they have lost in minutes.

Body temperatures rise (in some species) to over 110°F (43.3°C). After a short time at this temperature, most mammals start to suffer brain damage and then die, but desert mammals can remain at this temperature for several hours with no ill effects. No one is quite sure how they manage this, but probably it is by cooling blood in the arteries serving the brain. Veins in the head divide into smaller vessels that pass through the muzzle, where the blood is cooled, and the arteries lie adjacent to the cooler veins.

At night the body temperatures of some large desert mammals drop quite low. Allowing body temperatures to rise conserves water that would otherwise be lost as sweat or through panting.

HERBIVORES OF THE DESERT

It is scattered thinly, but there is plant food in the desert for any herbivorous animal hardy enough to find it. Among the herbivores of the desert are goats, sheep, wild asses, gazelles, antelopes, camels, and, in Australia, kangaroos and wallabies.

Several species of antelopes enter deserts, and the Arabian oryx (*Oryx leucoryx*) spends its entire life in the Arabian Desert. Antelopes generally live in rocky, mountainous areas, and they derive the water they need from plants. A particular desert shrub is an important item of their diet. During the day the shrub dries out almost completely, but at night it absorbs water from the air, so water accounts for 40 percent of its weight; that is when the antelopes eat it.

Water is provided in the tissues of plants (the water drips from a plant when it is crushed), but it is also supplemented by water that is

THE ARABIAN TAHR (*Hemitragus jayakari*) lives in the Arabian deserts of Oman. A goat-antelope, it looks and behaves like a goat, climbing and leaping easily over the mountainous terrain.

GAZELLES inhabit sandy deserts where they obtain most of the water they need from the plants they eat. The two species here are *(above left)* the Dorcas gazelle *(Gazella dorcas)* and *(above right)* the goitered gazelle *(G. subgutturosa)*. Both are found in the Sahara and the deserts of Asia.

HERMANN'S TORTOISE
(Testudo hermanni) lives in North Africa and southern Europe. It supplements its vegetarian diet with earthworms and snails. Tortoises shelter in deep burrows and emerge around dawn and dusk to feed.

produced chemically. When a quantity of starch is oxidized, the reaction produces an amount of water equal to about 60 percent of its original weight. Oxidizing fats produces even more water than this. So oxidizing foods inside the body is a good way of supplying water.

Most tortoises that live in the desert also obtain all the moisture they need from food. The American desert tortoise *(Gopherus agassizii)* has adapted a mechanism for storing water in an enlarged bladder.

Camels

No mammal is more firmly associated with the desert than the camel. Commonly used by people to transport heavy loads across the sands, they have earned the name "ships of the desert." Camels are herbivores, feeding on thorny plants and grasses.

There are two kinds of camel. The dromedary, or Arabian camel *(Camelus dromedarius)*, a single-humped camel, is found in the Middle East, India, and North Africa. The two-humped bactrian *(Camelus bactrianus)* is found in the highlands of central Asia and has a longer coat. The humps on their backs contain fat, which is used as an energy reserve.

The camel's ability to survive without water is legendary. The dromedary has been known to travel more than 300 miles (500 km) across the desert, taking up to three weeks to do so,

without drinking at all. A camel can lose up to 25 percent of its body weight, but it can drink water equal to 30 percent of its body weight (about 44 gallons, or 167 liters) in 10 minutes. Camels rarely drink during the winter. In summer, when water is available, they drink two or three times a week.

Camels have fur on their backs. In the bactrian camel this serves to keep it warm through the bitter winters in central Asia. For the dromedary the fur has a different purpose: it shades the skin and traps air. The temperature of the fur can reach more than 160°F (71°C), while the skin beneath it is at about 104°F (40°C). Camels sweat, but because their skin is shaded from the Sun, the sweat evaporates more slowly, by the heat of the animal's body rather than by solar heat.

Camels also have another way to keep cool. In the morning they lie on the ground, which has cooled overnight. Their thinly furred underside and legs are pressed against the ground, and only their protected backs are exposed. Sometimes groups of camels will lie with their sides pressed closely together. This also shields them from the Sun.

The camel is well suited to sandy conditions. Its broad two-toed feet spread its weight, making it easier to move over soft sand. Its rows of long eyelashes protect its eyes from the sand, and it can close off its nostrils.

"SHIPS OF THE DESERT." There are two species of Old World camel. Two-humped bactrian camels *(Camelus bactrianus) (top)* live in central Asia, some in the Gobi Desert. Single-humped dromedaries *(C. dromedarius) (bottom)* live in deserts in North Africa and the Middle East. They have also been introduced into Australia.

CARNIVORES OF THE DESERT

Desert hunters, which include cats, foxes, and snakes, feed mainly on rodents. Lions and cheetahs occasionally wander near the edges of deserts in Africa and Asia in search of gazelles. Most desert carnivores, however, are small; an animal about the size of a domestic cat has more chance than a big animal of finding shade.

The sand cat (*Felis margarita*) was discovered, about 150 years ago, near the border between Algeria and Libya. One was caught during an expedition led by the Frenchman General Margueritte, after whom it is named. The sand cat is a little smaller than the African wild cat (*F. libyca*)—an ancestor of the domestic cat. *F. libyca* lives in the deserts of Asia (where it is known as the Indian desert cat) as well as the North African desert. Its ears are large and widely spaced. This suggests keen hearing, but large ears also help keep the cat cool. (Mammals in the Arctic, by contrast, have small ears.)

Pallas's cat (*F. merula*) is gray rather than sand-colored. It lives throughout the deserts of Asia. The caracal, also called the desert lynx (*F. caracal*), is found in the deserts of Africa, the Middle East, and central and southwestern Asia and is recognizable by the tufts at the tips of its ears. It is nocturnal and hunts birds and mammals, including gazelles and hares.

Desert Foxes

Desert foxes are carnivores belonging to the dog family (Canidae), but much more versatile hunters than other dogs. They prefer small

THE SAND CAT *(Felis margarita)* *(left)* is found in the Sahara.

THE FENNEC FOX *(Vulpes zerda)* *(below)* lives in the deserts of North Africa and the Middle East.

mammals, but will eat almost anything they find, including worms, insects, and fruit. Foxes hunt small animals by stalking, then pouncing with a leap in the air that brings down their prey.

Three of the smallest foxes in the world live in deserts. All of them have huge ears to help keep them cool and to detect prey. The fennec (*Vulpes zerda*) inhabits the Sahara and deserts of the Middle East. No more than 16 inches (41 cm) long with an 8-inch (20-cm) tail, it spends the day in its burrow and hunts at night. Its North American equivalent is the kit fox (*V. macrotis*). The sand fox, or Rüppell's fox (*V. ruppelli*), lives in the driest regions of North Africa and Asia.

Insect Eaters

Desert scorpions live in burrows and hide in the shade of large rocks. They emerge at night to

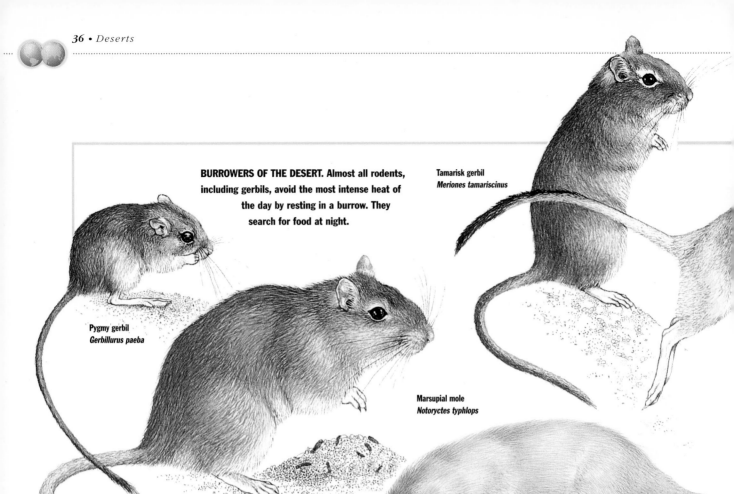

BURROWERS OF THE DESERT. Almost all rodents, including gerbils, avoid the most intense heat of the day by resting in a burrow. They search for food at night.

Tamarisk gerbil
Meriones tamariscinus

Pygmy gerbil
Gerbillurus paeba

Marsupial mole
Notoryctes typhlops

Great gerbil
Rhombomys opimus

attack passing insects, grabbing them with their pincers, and stinging them with deadly poison from their tails. Scorpions are, in turn, hunted by camel spiders, which live in underground burrows and also eat lizards and mice.

Adult antlions catch insects in flight, but their larvae (known as doodlebugs in the United States) do not even have to give chase to their prey. Instead, they dig a steep-sided pit and bury themselves with only their head protruding to await their prey. Any insect coming close to the rim is liable to fall down the slope and into the big, curved, open jaws waiting at the bottom. Some antlions throw sand grains with their heads

to prevent the prey from scrambling out of the trap.

Antlions belong to the family Myrmeleontidae, of the order Neuroptera, and physically they resemble dragonflies. They spend almost all their lives as larvae, living as adults only long enough to mate and lay eggs.

BURROWERS: MOLES AND RODENTS

Only one Australian mammal has taken up burrowing as a way of life. The marsupial mole (*Notoryctes typhlops*) is, in fact, a marsupial and

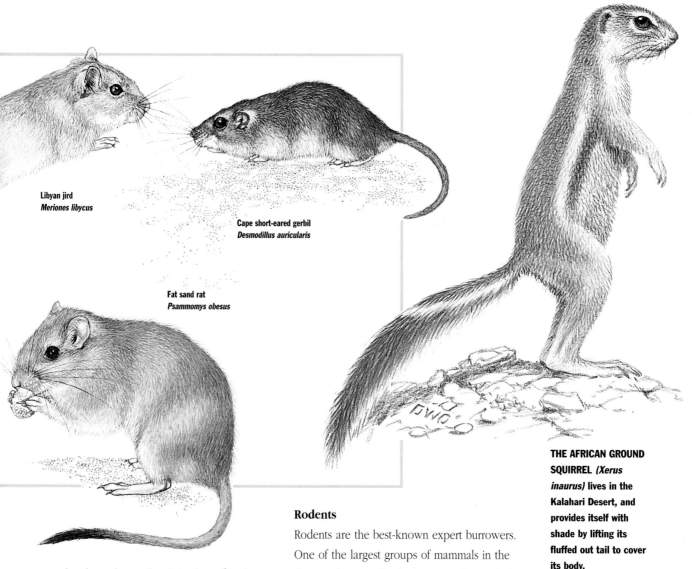

Libyan jird
Meriones libycus

Cape short-eared gerbil
Desmodillus auricularis

Fat sand rat
Psammomys obesus

THE AFRICAN GROUND
SQUIRREL *(Xerus
inaurus)* lives in the
Kalahari Desert, and
provides itself with
shade by lifting its
fluffed out tail to cover
its body.

Rodents

Rodents are the best-known expert burrowers.
One of the largest groups of mammals in the
deserts, they are also herbivores. They include
the jerboa, or desert, rat (family Dipodidae),
which is common in the Sahara, the kangaroo rat
(genus *Dipodomys*) of North America, and the
gerbil (*Gerbillus gerbillus*), now domesticated in
many countries, which comes from the sandy
deserts of northern China and Mongolia.

Almost all rodents seek food at night and
rest by day, usually in a burrow. This way of life
is admirably suited to desert conditions. Out in
the open there is no way an animal the size of a

not related to other moles. It is about 6 inches
(14 cm) long with a short tail and a curious
"shield" on the front of its head. This is the
naked skin (*rhinarium*) of its nose, toughened
and extended back to where its eyes would be if
it had any. Its shield allows the mole to shove
earth out of the way as it travels below ground.
Its "hands" have two huge claws used for
digging, and its hind feet have smaller claws
used to push earth away. The marsupial mole is
believed to feed on insects and their larvae.

rat could replenish the water it lost through evaporation, but in its burrow evaporation is reduced. The temperature below ground is low—in fact, cold may be more of a problem to a rodent than heat.

Rodents are very efficient at producing concentrated urine to conserve water. While camel urine is almost twice as concentrated as human urine, gerbil urine is nearly four times more concentrated. The Australian hopping mouse (*Notomys alexis*) excretes urine 6.5 times more concentrated than human urine.

Many desert rodents obtain all the water they need from their food. Bannertail kangaroo rats (*Dipodomys spectabilis*), which live in the North American desert, store large amounts of food in their burrows. Merriam's kangaroo rats (*D. merriami*) are not great provisioners, but they sneak into the burrows of bannertail kangaroo rats to steal food.

Hoarding food in burrows is useful not simply as a means of provisioning, but because it saves water. Dry plant material absorbs moisture from the damp air in the burrow, and by the time it is eaten, its water content is much higher. Wild gerbils, for example, store seeds. When they collect them, the seeds contain about 6 percent water by weight, but after they have been stored, this increases to about 30 percent.

Slowing Down

When food is scarce, some desert rodents have another trick: they become torpid for a few hours. Their breathing, heartbeat, and other bodily processes slow down, and their body temperature is allowed to fluctuate. In this state they use very little energy or water.

DESERT BIRDS

Birds have an average normal body temperature of about 104°F (40°C), several degrees higher than the 98.6°F (37°C) of mammals. Consequently, avoiding overheating is less of a problem for birds, because there is a smaller difference between their body temperature and the temperature of the air around them.

Birds generally have less difficulty finding water in desert regions. Those that can fly are able to travel as far as 30 miles (50 km) a day in search of water.

This is only part of the story, however. Birds are active in the heat of the day. Although adults of most bird species can fly, young fledglings cannot. Water must be brought to the nest by their parents.

Sandgrouse, desert birds of Africa and Asia, produce young that can find seeds soon after they hatch. But the fledglings also need water. The adults, especially males, have feathers on their bellies that uncurl when they are wet, trapping water. Early in the morning the males fly to the water hole, soak their feathers, then fly back to the nest, where the chicks peck at the feathers and drink the water.

Pigeons and doves, which are quite common in deserts, solve this problem in a different way. They feed their young on pigeon milk, also called crop milk. Both sexes lactate, or produce milk, under the stimulus of the hormone prolactin. It consists of water with protein and fat, and chemically it is very similar to mammalian milk. The milk provides the chicks with liquid as well as nourishment. For the first

MALE SANDGROUSE are more brightly colored than females. In this illustration *(right)* the males are shown on the left, and the females on the right.

Namaqua sandgrouse
Pterocles namaqua

Lichtenstein's sandgrouse
P. lichtensteinii

THE GREATER ROADRUNNER *(Geococcyx californianus)* of North America *(above)* feeds on small animals, including lizards, but snakes form an important part of its diet. It will kill and eat a rattlesnake.

few days of their lives this is all the food chicks receive. After that the parents start bringing them solid food, but their milk supply continues until the young are well grown.

Not surprisingly, young pigeons grow fast. In addition to their own bodily needs, parent birds must drink enough to produce milk, but this is not difficult for pigeons—desert mammals sometimes find lactation a severe strain.

Some birds have turned the desert plants to their advantage. In California and Arizona two species of woodpeckers, the Gila woodpecker (*Centurus uropygialis*) and the gilded flicker (*Colaptes chrysoides*), make holes in saguaro

cactus plants about 8 inches (20 cm) deep, with a chamber at the end. Abandoned woodpecker nests are used by a variety of other birds, including screech owls (*Otus asio*), elf owls (*Micrathene whitneyi*), and American sparrow hawks (*Falco sparverius*).

Non-Fliers

Not all desert birds fly well, and some do not fly at all. Coursers, several species in the genus *Cursorius*, are sandy-colored, long-legged birds of Old World deserts that stand upright and take to the air only when a predator comes too close. They feed mainly on insects.

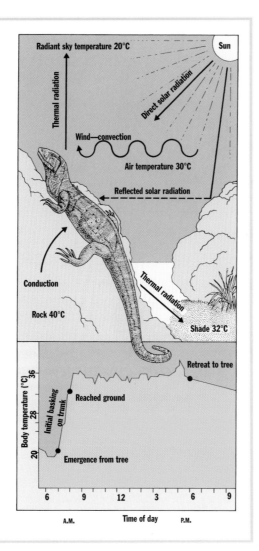

DESERT REPTILES must control their body temperature by finding areas within their environment that are appropriate for different times of day. They bask to warm their muscles at dawn, then use shade and the wind to cool them during the day. As the graph shows, once the lizard has warmed up, it maintains a fairly constant body temperature throughout the day, not very different from the 98.6°F (37°C) body temperature of a mammal. In this study the lizard's temperature was measured from a temperature-sensitive radio transmitter it had swallowed.

Radiant sky temperature 20°C

Sun

Thermal radiation

Direct solar radiation

Wind—convection

Air temperature 30°C

Reflected solar radiation

Conduction

Thermal radiation

Rock 40°C

Shade 32°C

Retreat to tree

Reached ground

Initial basking on trunk

Emergence from tree

Body temperature [°C]

36 28 20

6 9 12 3 6 9

A.M. Time of day P.M.

Roadrunners tackle larger prey. The greater roadrunner (*Geococcyx californianus*) lives in the southwestern United States, and the lesser roadrunner (*G. velox*) in Mexico and Central America. Closely related to the cuckoos, roadrunners can fly, although they spend most of their time on the ground. They earn their name from their habit of walking onto roads, then running away fast if disturbed. A greater roadrunner can reach speeds of 15 mph (24 km/h), an impressive pace for a bird barely 2 feet (60 cm) tall.

Roadrunners feed mainly on plants, insects, small vertebrates (animals with backbones), such as rodents and lizards, and eggs stolen from other ground-nesting birds. The greater roadrunner also eats snakes. It holds out a wing, allowing the snake to strike, then pounces.

THE MONITOR, the largest of all lizards, is active during the daytime. This Perentie monitor *(Varanus giganteus)* from Australia has sought shade to keep cool, and holds its body well clear of the hot ground.

DESERT REPTILES

Reptiles are cold-blooded vertebrates. Those that can be found in desert regions include tortoises, lizards, and snakes.

The fact that they are cold-blooded does not mean that they are cold, of course. It means that they cannot generate or regulate their body temperatures by the physiological means mammals and birds use: they cannot shiver to warm themselves or sweat to cool themselves, for example. They are called ectotherms; animals that can control their body temperatures are called endotherms.

For every reptile there is a range of tolerable temperatures. If the animal becomes colder or hotter than the limits of its range, it will die. Within the range there is a much narrower range—sometimes about 18°F (10°C), but for many lizards as little as 7°F (4°C)—within which it can be fully active. A reptile can keep its temperature within the range acceptable to it only by warming or cooling itself in some part of its environment that is at a suitable temperature.

There is an advantage, however. Birds and mammals use about 90 percent of the food they eat to provide the energy needed to maintain their body temperatures. Reptiles can use all the food they eat to grow and to repair their bodies. Since there is a limit to the amount of food needed for these purposes, in practice reptiles need to eat only about one-tenth of the amount of food that would be required to sustain a bird or mammal of similar size. This allows them ample time for moving to suitable areas and means that they can inhabit areas where food is scarce.

Like other desert animals, reptiles minimize water loss in excretion: they excrete nearly solid uric acid. Their impervious, scaly skins also help to reduce water loss.

Basking on Rocks

Early in the morning lizards and snakes bask on rocks in the desert. As soon as the Sun has warmed it, the animal will disappear. Around midday reptiles shelter in the deepest shade available to keep cool. It all sounds rather simple. In fact, it is very subtle.

The basking reptile presses its body against the rock on which it lies. The rock is warm, so the animal is warmed from below as well as from above. It is also warmed from the sides. It will have chosen a spot surrounded by other rocks that reflect sunlight—and heat—in its direction. Dust particles will also reflect heat, some of it in the animal's direction.

Convection from warmed surfaces transmits heat, and this also warms the reptile. However, the animal also loses heat by radiation and convection, and through the evaporation of water from its skin and respiratory passages. This does not matter, because early in the morning the reptile is cooler than its surroundings, so it gains more heat than it loses. Small adjustments in the position of its body allow a basking reptile to adjust its body temperature. Later in the day it may seek shade. Again, it chooses its shelter with care so it can achieve a comfortable temperature.

THE SIDEWINDER VIPER *(Bitis peringueyi)* *(opposite)* **lives in southern Africa. Its unusual method of locomotion leaves a characteristic trail.**

Expert Hunters

Snakes and many lizards have forked tongues, which act as extremely good indicators of both taste and smell. They continually monitor their surroundings and scent prey by flicking their tongues out into the air.

Many bury themselves in the sand in order to keep cool and to hide in wait for prey. McMahon's viper (*Eristocophis macmahonii*), for example, in the Asian deserts, buries itself in the sand, then lies, almost invisible, with just its eyes and nostrils above the surface.

All snakes are carnivorous, and many kill their prey with venom injected when the snake bites its prey, although the python famously squeezes its prey to death by suffocation.

Sidewinder Snakes

The ordinary movement of a snake is very like swimming, but for snakes in the desert loose sand presents difficulties. The sidewinder snake travels (at speed) sideways—at an angle of about 45° to the line of its body. It raises its head, throws it forward with the front half of its body following in a loop, and immediately raises its head again for the next "step." The movement also minimizes the contact made with the hot sand.

The true sidewinders are the small American rattlesnake, *Crotalus cerastes*, from the deserts of Mexico and the southwestern United States, the horned viper (*Cerastes cerastes*) of the Sahara and Asian Deserts, the carpet viper (*Echis carinatus*) of North Africa and the Middle East, and *Bitis peringueyi*, a small viper found in the deserts of southern Africa.

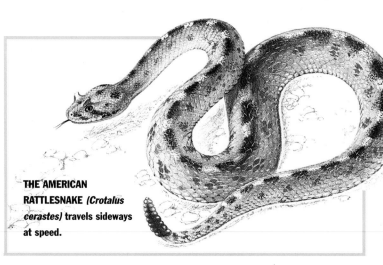

THE AMERICAN RATTLESNAKE *(Crotalus cerastes)* **travels sideways at speed.**

Desert Monitors

Monitors are large lizards with forked tongues like those of snakes. They are all classified in the genus *Varanus*, and together they comprise the family Varanidae. They occur throughout the Old World tropics, but are especially common in deserts. There are about 30 species, of which 24 occur in Australia, where they probably flourish because of the lack of competition from large mammalian carnivores.

Monitors are voracious predators that hunt by day, but they have to find shelter when the temperature rises too high. Gould's monitor, also called the sand monitor (*V. gouldi*), occurs throughout the deserts of Australia, living on the ground and sheltering in burrows during the hottest part of the day. This lizard is about 5 feet (1.5 m) long. It stands on its hind legs and hisses loudly when it feels threatened.

AFRICAN MIGRATORY LOCUSTS congregate into a swarm that may contain as many as 50 billion individuals. They will take to the air, then be carried where the wind takes them, alighting wherever they find vegetation.

Skinks

Skinks are a group of lizards of the family Scincidae, found in both the Old and New Worlds. Many species live in deserts, and some get about by "swimming" through loose sand like a fish. In fact, *Scincus philbyi*, a skink found in the deserts in the Middle East, is called the sandfish. The Florida sand skink (*Neoseps reynoldsi*), which lives among the sandhills of Florida, also travels in this way through sand.

Skinks hunt for insects and, like other lizards, dive into the sand when they are in danger. Some members of the skink family establish virtually permanent burrows.

DESERT INSECTS

Desert insects include ants, beetles, butterflies, cockroaches, flies, grasshoppers, and wasps. Many desert insects have an integument (outer covering), which reduces water loss through evaporation. Many of them do not drink, but get all the water they need from food.

Desert insects often lay their eggs after it has rained, and the larvae eat the desert plants that appear then. Honeypot ants collect so much nectar from the desert flowers that some of them swell up and serve as "repletes," from which the other ants feed.

The most notorious of all desert insects are locusts, which breed in marshy areas and then fly across vast distances, devouring all the plants in their wake. There are several species, all of them serious pests, but the desert locust (*Schistocerca gregaria*) and the African migratory locust (*Locusta migratoria*) cause the greatest

damage, destroying vast crop areas when they land on farmland. Of these two the desert locust is the more difficult to control, because it can breed in any suitable location within a range that extends from the Atlantic coast of Africa to India. The African migratory locust breeds only in certain places and is confined to Africa.

Desert locusts live most of the time as solitary individuals. Young ones, called hoppers, are green; adults are brown, and both look like grasshoppers—which is what they are. From time to time, however, they congregate, and if they become densely crowded, their behavior and appearance change. Green hoppers turn black and orange, and brown adults turn yellow. When they have entered their gregarious phase, they form a swarm of up to 50 billion insects. They are not strong fliers, so their swarm drifts with the wind, but when they see green vegetation, they land and devour every last leaf of it.

The two phases differ so much that people used to think that they were separate species. They caused fear in rural communities; the soil would come alive with hoppers stretching to the horizon, and the swarms seemed to appear from nowhere, darkening the sky.

CACTI are a valuable source of food and water for many animals of the American deserts. Here, a nymph of the grasshopper *Taenipoda auricornis* feeds on the fruit of the cactus *Melocactus elessertianus* in the Mexican desert.

Survival of the Deserts

The Earth is changing constantly, and some regions that are now deserts were once fertile farmlands. As climatic change continues, the deserts will increase or decrease in size.

The semiarid lands surrounding the deserts suffer from periods of drought, and the harsh conditions for crops mean that they are vulnerable farming areas. Working the land until its fertility is exhausted (overcropping) and using it too intensively for animals (overgrazing), together with the removal of trees (often chopped down for fuel and building materials), all cause erosion. As the cultivated and natural vegetation disappears, the plants' roots no longer bind soil particles together. Dried to dust, the soil blows away in the wind, and may bury plants. Gradually, the desert spreads. Poor irrigation also contributes to the effect.

In the 1970s the United Nations labeled the process "desertification." The United Nations Environment Program (UNEP) estimates that 8.9 billion acres (3.6 billion hectares) of land are at risk. This amounts to nearly one quarter of the land area of the world, affecting about one in six of the world's population. Satellite images lend weight to the trend; these show that in 1990 the Sahara was about 245,000 square miles (635,000 sq. km) larger than it was in 1980.

At present there is a risk that the Sahara may expand southward into what is now the Sahel region. This covers part of Senegal, Mauritania, Burkina Faso, Mali, Niger, Chad, Sudan, and Ethiopia. They are among the poorest countries in the world, where people are dependent on farming and the pressure on the land is considerable.

Australia is also at risk. As with the Sahara, these deserts are surrounded by semiarid lands where the rainfall is unreliable. Without careful management much of this area might deteriorate into true desert.

Desertification is not the only factor that could change the deserts. Changes in the so-called greenhouse effect could increase rainfall, which would result in quite different effects.

THE GREENHOUSE EFFECT

Heat and visible light are forms of energy that travel as radiation. They cross space as waves, and the only difference between heat and light is the distance between the top of one wave and the top of the next. This is called their wavelength. Light can be split into its component colors, called the visible spectrum, and the wavelengths of light vary according to the color. Violet light has a shorter wavelength than red light. Ultraviolet light has wavelengths shorter than those of violet light. All of them are shorter than the wavelength of heat. (X rays and gamma rays are also forms of radiation, but have wavelengths that are shorter than those of light.)

Air is transparent to short-wave radiation, so when the Sun shines, its rays pass through the air without interruption and warm the surface of

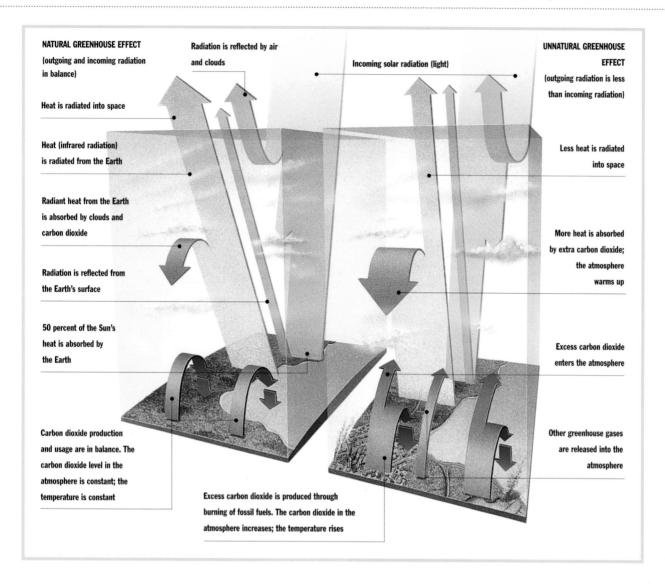

NATURAL GREENHOUSE EFFECT (outgoing and incoming radiation in balance)

Heat is radiated into space

Heat (infrared radiation) is radiated from the Earth

Radiant heat from the Earth is absorbed by clouds and carbon dioxide

Radiation is reflected from the Earth's surface

50 percent of the Sun's heat is absorbed by the Earth

Carbon dioxide production and usage are in balance. The carbon dioxide level in the atmosphere is constant; the temperature is constant

Radiation is reflected by air and clouds

Incoming solar radiation (light)

Excess carbon dioxide is produced through burning of fossil fuels. The carbon dioxide in the atmosphere increases; the temperature rises

UNNATURAL GREENHOUSE EFFECT (outgoing radiation is less than incoming radiation)

Less heat is radiated into space

More heat is absorbed by extra carbon dioxide; the atmosphere warms up

Excess carbon dioxide enters the atmosphere

Other greenhouse gases are released into the atmosphere

the land and sea. When they are warmed, the land and sea start to radiate heat themselves, but the radiation they emit has a longer wavelength than those of the light or heat from the Sun, and the air is not entirely transparent to it.

Some gases, especially water vapor and carbon dioxide, but also methane, ozone, and nitrous oxide, absorb this long-wave heat. They then begin to radiate heat in all directions—some into space, some to the sides, and some back toward the Earth. Most of the radiation strikes other molecules and warms the air.

During the day the Sun warms the Earth. The Earth radiates this heat back into space, but some of it warms the air. Some of the heat escapes, but in the day heat is reaching the Earth (as sunshine) faster than it is being radiated away. This makes the air warmer.

At night the Earth continues to radiate away its own warmth, so the Earth and the air grow cooler. Before they cool completely, however, the Sun rises again, and the warming resumes. The result is that the Earth's atmosphere is warmer than it would be if it did not contain

THE GREENHOUSE EFFECT. It is the unbalanced greenhouse effect that causes concern. During the Earth's history the atmospheric concentration of carbon dioxide has fluctuated many times. These changes have been associated with climate change.

DESERTIFICATION. Large areas of the world are at risk from desertification, and developing countries are particularly under threat. Among the consequences of the spread of the deserts are the loss of productive land and widespread risk of famine. The process can be halted by practices such as reforestation (planting trees in the area) and growing drought-resistant crops. Small-scale local initiatives are important in solving this global problem.

those heat-trapping gases. This is called the greenhouse effect because it is a little like what happens in a greenhouse. Heat can enter through the glass, but it is unable to leave, so the air inside becomes warmer than the air outside. (What actually happens is that the air inside the greenhouse is unable to mix with the air outside, which is not what happens in the atmosphere.)

Scientists have measured the amount of radiation the Sun emits and the proportion of it that strikes the Earth. If there were no heat-trapping gases to delay the cooling of the air, the average temperature at the surface of the Earth would be –9.4°F (–23°C). In fact, the average temperature at the surface is about 59°F (15°C), so the greenhouse effect makes the Earth about 68.4°F (38°C) warmer than it would be otherwise.

Eventually, of course, all the warmth we receive from the Sun is radiated back into space. The energy we receive precisely balances the energy we lose. Were this not so, the Earth would grow steadily hotter or colder. The greenhouse effect merely delays the loss of heat, but that delay is very important.

Without the greenhouse effect life on Earth would be very uncomfortable. The oceans would be covered by thick sheets of ice, except in the tropics, and there would be very few places on land where plants could grow. But many scientists now fear we may be adding to the natural greenhouse effect, and that this could lead to an "enhanced greenhouse effect."

The main so-called greenhouse gas that causes the enhanced greenhouse effect is carbon dioxide, released by burning fossil fuels such as

ATLANTIC OCEAN

PACIFIC OCEAN

coal, oil, and natural gas. Methane, released from leaking gas pipes and from cattle and sheep farming, nitrous oxide, and ozone, produced by chemical reactions among the exhaust gases from automobiles, are also greenhouse gases.

These gases are accumulating in the air and may absorb more and more of the outgoing radiation so that gradually the climates of the world would become warmer. Were the concentration of these gases to double, scientists calculate that the average temperature would rise by 1.8–6.3°F (1–3.5°C), the most likely increase being about 3.6°F (2°C). At the present rate at

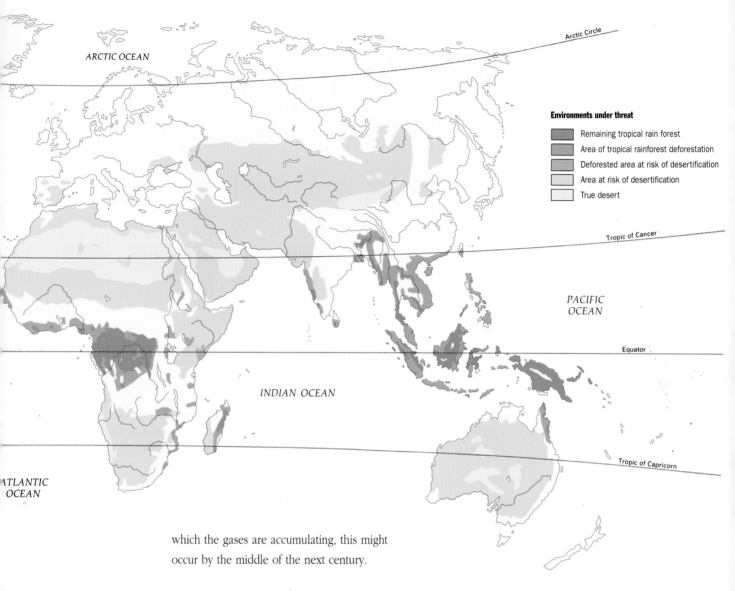

Environments under threat

Remaining tropical rain forest
Area of tropical rainforest deforestation
Deforested area at risk of desertification
Area at risk of desertification
True desert

which the gases are accumulating, this might occur by the middle of the next century.

Warmer Climates

So far there is no proof that climates are growing warmer. Records from weather stations suggest that the average temperature has risen by about 1°F (0.5°C) since 1880, but most of this increase happened around 1920. Satellite measurements show that the Earth has cooled a little since 1980, most strongly in the Arctic. Some scientists believe that if we continue releasing greenhouse gases at the present rate, any warming that occurs will be in the lower end of the range—

the temperature rise would be about 1.8°F (1°C) at most by about 2100.

The consequences of warmer climates are far from certain. The prediction is that warming will occur most strongly in high latitudes, with little or no change in the tropics. This means that the climate of what are now hot deserts will be affected. A general rise in temperature will increase the rate at which water evaporates from the oceans. If the air is more moist, more cloud will form, shading the surface, and so offsetting part of the warming. More cloud also means more rain. It is possible that rainfall will increase in the low-latitude deserts. Paintings made between 7,000 and 8,000 years ago on rocks and in caves in the Sahara depict crocodiles, buffalos, elephants, deer, and people hunting hippopotamus. Clearly, the climate then was much wetter, and almost certainly warmer, than it is now.

Warming could cause the equatorial climate belt to expand, bringing more humidity to the deserts, but displacing the belt of dry, tropical climate into higher latitudes. In that case the Sahara would become wetter, but southern Europe drier (although probably less dry than the present desert because of the increase in rainfall). In North America the northern margin of the desert might shift to about the latitude of Oregon, but the wheat-growing belt might extend much farther into Canada.

Heat is transported from the equator to the poles by the movement of the air and also by ocean currents. Were the climate to grow warmer, the present pattern of currents might alter. In particular, the circulation in the Atlantic might change radically, so the Gulf Stream would become weaker, and the part of it that branches off as the North Atlantic Drift would no longer bathe the coasts of northwestern Europe.

This would in turn make European climates much colder. A change of this sort occurred thousands of years ago. Just as climates were warming rapidly at the end of the last ice age, they were twice suddenly plunged back into ice-age conditions, each time for about 1,000 years. This change in the North Atlantic circulation (and failure of the North Atlantic Drift) is believed to

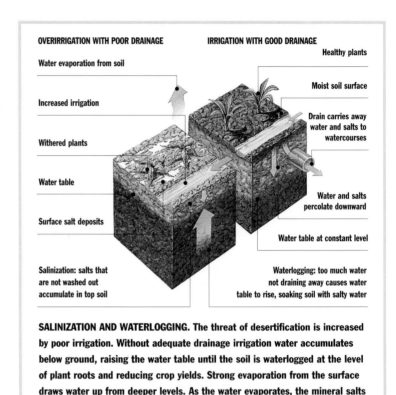

OVERIRRIGATION WITH POOR DRAINAGE

Water evaporation from soil

Increased irrigation

Withered plants

Water table

Surface salt deposits

Salinization: salts that are not washed out accumulate in top soil

IRRIGATION WITH GOOD DRAINAGE

Healthy plants

Moist soil surface

Drain carries away water and salts to watercourses

Water and salts percolate downward

Water table at constant level

Waterlogging: too much water not draining away causes water table to rise, soaking soil with salty water

SALINIZATION AND WATERLOGGING. The threat of desertification is increased by poor irrigation. Without adequate drainage irrigation water accumulates below ground, raising the water table until the soil is waterlogged at the level of plant roots and reducing crop yields. Strong evaporation from the surface draws water up from deeper levels. As the water evaporates, the mineral salts from the underlying rock remain, accumulating in the soil, sometimes to levels high enough to poison plants and render the land sterile.

have been the cause of the change.

Plants might adapt to a higher concentration of carbon dioxide and warmer temperatures by opening their stomata for shorter periods. This would reduce the amount of water evaporating from their leaf surfaces, allowing them to use water more efficiently. Plants might be able to grow in places that otherwise would be too dry for them, and as the area of vegetation increased, plants would remove more of the carbon dioxide from the air.

It is much too early to tell whether warming due to an enhanced greenhouse effect has already begun, and it is still not certain that it

GOATS AND SHEEP FORAGE among sparse vegetation in Morocco. Government programs have encouraged nomadic peoples to settle, increasing the number of animals on the land and contributing to soil erosion and desertification.

will happen at all. Nevertheless, most scientists are agreed that we must take steps to reduce the greenhouse gases released into the air.

OVERGRAZING

For centuries nomadic peoples have raised livestock in the lands bordering deserts. In the past they drove mixed herds of cattle, sheep, goats, camels, and horses along routes that followed the rains from one area of grazing to the next. It was a poor, hazardous life, in which a failure of the rains could mean ruin for families who measured their wealth by the size of their herds and flocks. The herds and flocks were

OVERGRAZING. The removal of vegetation by grazing and for burning as domestic fuel can cause erosion and transform poor grassland into desert.

The original savanna (open grassland) is a mixture of grasses and small trees

Heavy use of the land for grazing destroys the best grasses; the area is invaded by poor grasses and thorn bushes. The soil becomes compacted, causing erosion

Continued grazing removes the remaining grasses, and thorns take over. Erosion is more rapid

Large gullies are cut by the rain, and the land becomes unusable for grazing

often large, but they were also very mixed, and this allowed them to use the pasture very efficiently. Cattle prefer tufts of grass and leaves of trees and shrubs that grow within their reach. Sheep prefer short grass. Goats will eat either. The species did not compete with each other.

Several developments contributed to change the lives of the nomads. The first was the improved health of their livestock. At one time many animals used to die from complaints an American or European veterinarian could easily cure. Veterinary services reached the remote areas and were welcomed. Killer diseases were conquered, fewer animals died, and people were more prosperous because their herds and flocks increased in size.

Far from the borders of the desert some of the city dwellers also became more prosperous. As their fortunes improved, so did their diets. They ate more meat. The traders supplying the meat had to increase the supply, so they went to the nomadic herders and bought from them.

Once again, the prosperity of the herders improved, and naturally they raised still more animals, partly to meet the increased demand for meat and partly because they measured their wealth in the number of animals they owned. This did not simply increase the size of their herds, it also changed their composition. There were now more cattle, so there was heavier grazing of the tufts of grass that cattle prefer.

Governments sought to help the nomads by encouraging them to settle. Living in towns, they would have access to medical and other services, and their children could go to school. As tending livestock was the only way of life they knew, they brought their animals with them.

Increasing the size of herds and flocks, and concentrating livestock around the villages, combined to damage and in places destroy the pasture. The cattle ate the best grasses and herbs and the leaves from shrubs and lowest branches of trees. Sheep nibbled the grasses lower. Increasingly, goats were the only animals that could find enough to eat. They climbed trees, stripped them of foliage, and uprooted and ate grasses and herbs.

When it did rain, the soil had no protection and its surface layers washed away. The land eroded and became desert.

People often blame goats for the damage they cause, but it is not really their fault, nor that of the owners. Once the pasture has deteriorated beyond a certain point, goats are the only animals it will support, so people have no choice but to raise goats in preference to other animals.

SALINIZATION AND WATERLOGGING

Where the climate is dry, the land can be induced to grow crops if water is brought to it. This is irrigation, and farmers have been practicing it throughout history.

Irrigation is essential, of course, but unless provision is made to remove excess water, it can cause serious damage, and contribute to the spread of the deserts. Water applied to the surface of soil soaks down through the soil until it reaches a layer of impermeable clay or rock. Then it begins to flow downhill, very slowly, by filling the spaces between soil particles. On the surface, however, the soil remains dry once the water has gone, so it seems sensible to pour on

DESERTIFICATION IN THE SAHARA. The large semiarid region south of the Sahara, the Sahel, is at risk from desertification as a result of modern farming methods and the growth of cities, which place a strain on water supplies.

DESERTIFICATION IN AUSTRALIA. The country has a fairly dry climate, and much of the interior of the country is desert. Large semiarid grassland regions could be threatened with desertification as a result of their conversion to grazing land.

Tunis

Algiers

Rabat • Saharan Atlas

MOROCCO TUNISIA

Tripoli

High Atlas

Grand Erg Occidental

El Aai n

WESTERN
SAHARA
(occupied by
Morocco)

ALGERIA

Grand Erg Oriental

Ahaggar Mts

Erg
Chech

S A H A R A

A r

Tibesti

MAURITANIA

Nouakchott

MALI

NIGER

Niamey •

Bamako •

Lake
Chad

CHAD

N'Djamena

Cairo

Nile

LIBYA

Libyan
Desert

EGYPT

L. Nasser

Nubian
Desert

Bodele

Athara

ERITREA

Khartoum • Asmera

Blue Nile

SUDAN

White Nile

Ethiopian
Highlands

Addis Ababa

Sudd

ETHIOPIA

DJIBOUTI
Djibouti

Ogaden

Shebelle

SOMALIA

Juba

Mogadishu •

Cape
Blanc

Senegal

Niger

Areas at risk of desertification

Very high

High

Moderate

True desert

Melville I

Darwin •

Arnhem Land

Torres Strait
Cape York

Gulf
of
Carpentaria

Cape
York
Peninsula

Great Barrier Reef

Kimberley
Plateau

Tanami
Desert

Barkly Tableland

Great Dividing Range

Great Sandy
Desert

Hamersley
Range

Macdonnell
Ranges
• Alice Springs

Selwyn Range

Gibson Desert

Musgrave
Ranges

Simpson
Desert

Great
Artesian
Basin

Fraser Island

AUSTRALIA

Brisbane

Great Victoria Desert

Lake Eyre

Grey Range

L Barlee

Lake
Torrens

Darling

L Moore

Lake Gairdner

Perth •

Darling Range

Nullarbor Plain

Eyre
Peninsula

Murray

Murrumbidgee

Sydney

Adelaide

Canberra

Great Australian Bight

Kangaroo
Island

Australian Alps

Melbourne

King Island

Bass Strait

Furneaux
Group

Tasmania

more. That, too, sinks through the soil to join the water that has not yet had time to drain out of the area. The upper margin of the wetted soil—the water table—gradually rises.

Eventually, as more water is poured onto the soil, the water table rises to the level in the soil where it surrounds the roots of crop plants. Plant roots must respire, and for that they need air, but with the soil around them saturated this is impossible; the crops drown in soil that has become waterlogged.

As water moves through the soil, it dissolves mineral salts from the rock particles. When water is poured onto the surface, it fills all the tiny spaces between soil particles. At first it drains downward, but once the water table has risen to a certain level, the movement changes. Now evaporation at the surface draws up more water from below. The water is a weak solution of mineral salts, but when water evaporates, any substances dissolved in it are left behind. Salts accumulate near the surface of the soil and around the plant roots, where they draw moisture out.

Crop seedlings are particularly vulnerable to this process of salinization. Waterlogging can be avoided if drains are installed at the same time as the irrigation system, but salinization remains a problem in many semiarid areas.

HARVESTING THE WATER

When rain falls, some of the water evaporates and the remainder drains downward through the soil until it reaches a layer of impermeable rock or clay. There it accumulates, filling all the spaces between soil particles to become ground water. Water reaching the surface produces an oasis. The land around it is very fertile and is often densely populated by plants and people. Cultivated areas around oases can be large—sometimes over 500 square miles (1,295 sq. km).

Not all oases are natural, however. Many are watered by wells sunk into the ground water, and others by water flowing through underground tunnels. Called a qanat system, it comprises gently sloping tunnels dug into an alluvial fan (the fan-shaped zone of deposits from former rivers) until the water table is located. The tunnels are then extended into the saturated soil. Water flows through the tunnel under gravity, emerging as a spring in a natural hollow. This allows the land around the spring to be cultivated. The technique was devised 3,000 years ago, and some qanats are still in use.

Qanats are expensive to build and maintain, and they have now been superseded by modern irrigation systems. These consist of pipes with nozzles at intervals along them through which irrigation water is pumped. The pipes are laid so the nozzles deliver controlled amounts of water to the soil near the roots of the crop plants.

HARVESTING RAINWATER. In the Thar Desert, on the border of India and Pakistan, up to 10 inches (250 mm) of rain falls in the space of about a week in the monsoons in summer. The rainfall is so heavy that water would flow over the surface and away, instead of soaking into the ground. To prevent this, farmers have built dams across valleys. Water is held behind the dams, where it soaks into the ground. When it has gone, the land is still moist and fertile.

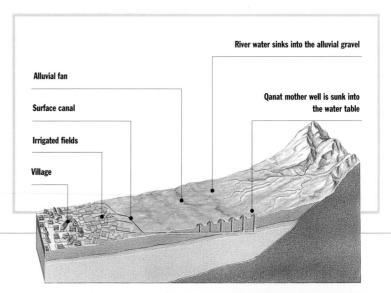

Alluvial fan

Surface canal

Irrigated fields

Village

River water sinks into the alluvial gravel

Qanat mother well is sunk into the water table

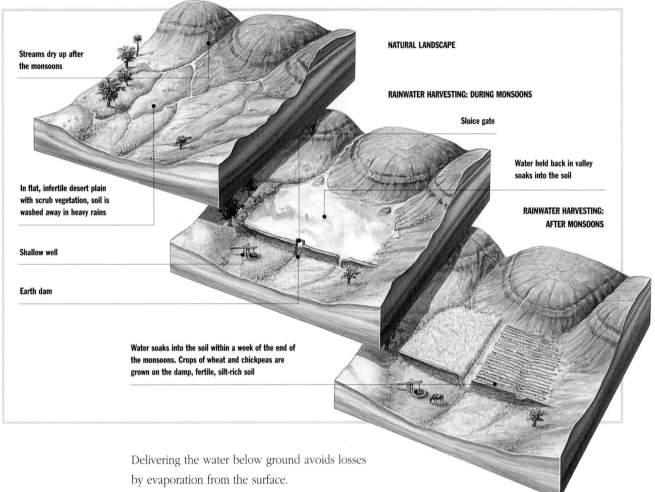

Streams dry up after
the monsoons

In flat, infertile desert plain
with scrub vegetation, soil is
washed away in heavy rains

Shallow well

Earth dam

Water soaks into the soil within a week of the end of
the monsoons. Crops of wheat and chickpeas are
grown on the damp, fertile, silt-rich soil

NATURAL LANDSCAPE

RAINWATER HARVESTING: DURING MONSOONS

Sluice gate

Water held back in valley
soaks into the soil

RAINWATER HARVESTING:
AFTER MONSOONS

**QANAT IRRIGATION.
About 3,000 years ago,
people started using
underground water in the
Sahara to make artificial
oases. They dug sloping
tunnels, which filled with
water when they crossed
the water table. This
flowed down to a network
of irrigation canals in a
natural hollow, providing
water for crops.**

Delivering the water below ground avoids losses
by evaporation from the surface.

Some traditional irrigation methods are
based on trapping moisture in shallow surface
depressions. In Arizona the Hopi developed a
farming system of this kind, growing corn,
beans, and squashes in hollows that collected
moisture. During the brief rainy season Sudanese
farmers grow sorghum, their most important
crop, in the same way. In Israel there are
orchards in which each small tree grows in a
hollow dug in the surface, the plants being
widely separated like the shrubs that grow
naturally in the desert.

The Thar Desert of India and Pakistan
receives 5–10 inches (130–250 mm) of rainfall a
year, all of it in the space of about a week in
summer. The rain is so heavy that the ground

cannot absorb it.
Farmers capture the water by means of dams
built of earth. The water is held behind the
dams, where it has time to soak into the ground
and can be used to irrigate crops.

Developing new farming methods requires
investment of time and money. When people are
desperately poor, they cannot afford to look
toward the long-term future. Only where people
are more prosperous—and where they control
the land and have a stake in the future—can
they plan. Much environmental damage in the
world is a symptom of poverty. We must hope
that by tackling this we can solve the problems
facing farmers in extreme environments, in the
deserts and elsewhere.

Glossary

albedo The reflectivity of a surface, measured as the proportion of the light striking it that is reflected.

alga A simple green plant that lacks true leaves, stem, and root. Many algae are single-celled; some are multicelled. Seaweeds are algae.

alluvial fan Sediment deposited by a river where it flows onto almost level ground and its water slows, losing energy. The deposit has an approximately triangular shape, its width increasing with distance downstream, and it remains after the river has dried and disappeared.

amphibian A vertebrate animal of the class Amphibia. The young develop in water, although the adults may live on land. Frogs, toads, newts, and salamanders are amphibians.

areole 1 A small, raised area on the stem of a cactus from which a flower or spine arises. **2** An area on a leaf that is enclosed by veins.

arroyo A dry, steep-sided gully through soft sedimentary rock formed by a river that flows following rain.

bacteria Microscopic organisms, most of which are single-celled, that are found in air, water, and soil everywhere. Different types vary in shape and way of life.

barchan A crescent-shaped sand dune, the "horns" of the crescent pointing downwind. Barchans form where the wind varies to either side of a prevailing direction, and the supply of sand is limited.

biome A large region throughout which living conditions for plants and animals are broadly similar, so the region can be classified according to its vegetation type.

butte An isolated, steep-sided, flat-topped hill.

carnivore An animal that feeds exclusively on other animals.

chlorophyll The green pigment, found in most plants, that absorbs light energy. This is then used to drive the reactions of photosynthesis.

consumer An organism that is unable to manufacture its own food from simple ingredients but must obtain it by eating (consuming) other organisms.

convection Transfer of heat through a liquid or gas by the movement of the liquid or gas.

desert pavement A desert surface composed of exposed bedrock or closely packed gravel or stones. Also called a "reg."

draa A ridge of sand or linked chain of dunes usually more than 1,000 feet (300 m) high and located between 500 yards (460 m) and 3 miles (5 km) from its nearest neighbor.

dust devil A rising, spiraling flow of air that raises fine dust particles into a column up to about 300 feet (90 m) high. It is a small version of a whirlwind.

ecology The study of the relationships among living organisms in a defined area and between the organisms and the nonliving features of their surroundings.

ecosystem A community of living organisms and their nonliving environment within a defined area. This may be of any size. A forest may be studied as an ecosystem and so may a drop of water.

ectotherm An animal that maintains a fairly constant body temperature by behavioral means, such as basking or seeking shade. Reptiles are ectotherms.

eluviation The removal of soluble substances from the upper layers of soil and their deposition at a lower level.

endotherm An animal in which a fairly constant internal body temperature is maintained by physiological means, such as sweating, shivering, and the contraction and dilation of blood vessels. Birds and mammals are endotherms.

ephemeral Appearing only briefly and soon disappearing.

erg A vast expanse of desert sand; a "sand sea."

eutrophic Highly enriched in nutrients.

fungus A soft-bodied organism that obtains nutrients by absorbing them from its surroundings. Fungi are neither plants nor animals but constitute a kingdom of their own, the Fungi.

greenhouse effect The warming of the lower atmosphere due to the absorption by certain atmospheric gases of heat radiated from the surface. The natural greenhouse effect maintains a surface temperature 68°F (38°C) warmer than it would be in the absence of any greenhouse effect. Some scientists fear that the continued emission of "greenhouse gases" resulting from human activities may cause an enhanced greenhouse effect leading to a warming of the global climate.

ground water Water below ground that fills all the spaces between soil particles, thus saturating the soil.

harmattan A dry, dusty wind that blows from the east or northeast in Africa between January and July. It usually occurs north of the equator, but occasionally south of the equator.

herbivore An animal that feeds exclusively on plants.

insectivore An animal that feeds mainly or exclusively on insects.

inselberg Literally, an "island mountain" (German); an isolated, steep-sided hill standing on a plain.

invertebrate An animal that does not have a backbone.

kanat *See* qanat.

khamsin A hot, dusty, dry wind that blows from North Africa across Egypt, usually between April and June. Strong southerly or southwesterly winds over the Red Sea are also called khamsins.

lichen A plantlike organism consisting of a fungus and either an alga or a cyanobacterium (a bacterium that carries out photosynthesis) living in close association. The visible part of a lichen may be crustlike, scaly, leafy, or shrubby.

mesa A steep-sided, flat-topped hill made from horizontal layers of sedimentary rock. A mesa is bigger than a butte but smaller than a plateau.

oasis A desert area where water is available throughout the year (it is usually supplied by ground water), and plants are able to grow.

omnivore An animal that eats food derived from both plants and animals.

ouadi The Arabic name for the usually dry bed of a river, also spelled "wadi."

pediment A gently sloping surface between the foot of a hill and a plain.

photorespiration A series of chemical reactions that occurs in the photosynthesizing cells of many plants. Carbon is absorbed, as in respiration, but without any release of energy. It is therefore wasteful of carbon.

photosynthesis The series of chemical reactions by which green plants manufacture sugars, obtaining hydrogen from water and carbon from carbon dioxide, the energy driving the reactions being provided by light that is absorbed by chlorophyll.

plateau An area of flat, elevated land.

playa A flat, low-lying area with a surface of evaporite deposits laid down by evaporation following occasional, but repeated, flooding with salty water.

predator An organism that obtains food by consuming another organism. Most predators are animals that chase, overpower, and kill their prey, but insectivorous plants are also predators.

producer An organism, such as a green plant, that assembles large, complex substances from simple ingredients. On land the principal producers are green plants and in water they are single-celled plants called phytoplankton.

qanat An irrigation system consisting of underground tunnels that channel water to a low-lying area where it accumulates to produce an artificial oasis. Qanats have been dug in many parts of the Sahara and Middle East, but especially in Iran. The word is also spelled "kanat."

respiration 1 The oxidation of carbon to carbon dioxide in cells with the release of energy. **2** The action of breathing.

Sahel The semiarid land along the southern border of the Sahara, occupying part of Senegal, Mauritania, Burkina Faso, Mali, Niger, Chad, Sudan, and Ethiopia.

scavenger An animal that feeds on dead material, such as fallen plant or animal remains.

seif dune A linear or longitudinal sand dune that forms where the wind varies to either side of a prevailing direction, and there is an abundant supply of sand.

sirocco A strong, sometimes gale-force wind that blows out of the northern Sahara, affecting lands bordering the Mediterranean. The wind is dry and warm, but gathers moisture as it crosses the sea and can bring humid weather in the lands of the Aegean and Adriatic.

stoma (plural stomata) A small pore in a leaf through which gases can pass and from which water evaporates.

succulent 1 (noun) A plant that stores water in cells in its swollen stem or leaves and conserves water by having adaptations such as leaves that are rolled or reduced to spines, or have stomata set in pits. **2** (adjective) Fleshy.

transpiration The loss of water vapor through pores, called stomata in the leaves and lenticels in the stems, of green plants.

transverse dune A long sand dune lying at right angles to the wind. Transverse dunes form, usually as a series of parallel dunes, where the wind blows nearly always from one direction, and there is an abundant supply of sand.

tropics Those parts of the world that lie between latitudes 23°30'N and 23°30'S. These latitudes mark the boundaries of the region within which the Sun is directly overhead at noon on at least one day each year. The Tropic of Cancer is to the north of the equator and the Tropic of Capricorn to the south.

vertebrate An animal that has a backbone. Vertebrates also have a bony skull containing the brain and a skeleton made from bone or cartilage. Fish, amphibians, reptiles, birds, and mammals are vertebrates.

wadi *See* ouadi.

water table The uppermost margin of the ground water, below which the soil is saturated and above which it is not, although it is wet.

weathering The physical and chemical processes by which rocks and minerals are broken down to particles of varying sizes, and soluble compounds are released into water.

weathering rind A partly weathered layer on the outside of a rock that is often colored yellow, orange, or red due to the oxidation of minerals containing iron.

whirlwind A fierce but very local wind storm in which air spirals upward carrying dust particles and sand grains, sometimes to a height of 6,500 feet (2,000 m); it is a large, more violent version of a dust devil. Whirlwinds often occur in groups, new ones appearing as old ones die. They rise upward from the ground (unlike tornadoes that descend from a cloud).

Further Reading

Basics of Environmental Science by Michael Allaby. Routledge.

Biology by Neil A. Campbell. The Benjamin/Cummings Publishing Co. Inc.

The Encyclopedia of Birds edited by Christopher M. Perrins and Alex L.A. Middleton. Facts on File.

The Encyclopedia of Insects edited by Christopher O'Toole. Facts on File.

The Encyclopedia of Mammals edited by David Macdonald. Facts on File.

The Encyclopedia of Reptiles and Amphibians edited by Tim Halliday and Kraig Adler. Facts on File.

Flowering Plants of the World edited by V.H. Heywood. Oxford University Press, New York.

Green Planet edited by David M. Moore. Cambridge University Press.

The Hunters by Philip Whitfield. Simon and Schuster.

Hutchinson Encyclopedia of the Earth edited by Peter J. Smith. Hutchinson.

The Lie of the Land edited by K.J. Gregory. Oxford University Press, New York.

Longman Illustrated Animal Encyclopedia edited by Philip Whitfield. Guild Publishing.

The Oxford Encyclopedia of Trees of the World edited by Bayard Hora. Oxford University Press, New York.

Planet Earth: Cosmology, Geology, and the Evolution of Life and Environment by Cesare Emiliani. Cambridge University Press.

Snakes of the World by Chris Mattison. Blandford Press Ltd.

The Science of Ecology by Richard Brewer. Saunders College Publishing, Harcourt Brace College Publishers.

Dangerous Weather: Drought by Michael Allaby. Facts on File.

The Desert by John Cloudsley-Thompson. Orbis Publishing.

Web sites:

Deserts: Geology and Resources is a site belonging to the U.S. Geological Survey at: http://pubs.usgs.gov/gip.deserts/

Gander Academy, Deserts Theme is a Canadian educational site with information about desert wildlife at: http://www.stemnet.nf.ca/CITE/deserts.htm

Photographic Acknowledgments

7 EOSAT/British Aerospace; **8–9** Christine Delpal/Explorer; **11** Arthur Gloor/Oxford Scientific Films; **17** Gerald Cubitt; **18** Hans Christian Heap/Planet Earth Pictures; **19** Christine Osborne Pictures; **31** Fredrik Ehrenstrom/Oxford Scientific Films; **40–41** Greg Fyfe/Australian Nature Transparencies; **43** Anthony Bannister Photo Library; **44** Gunter Ziesler/Bruce Coleman Limited; **45** K.G. Preston-Mafham/Premaphotos Wildlife; **51** Christine Osborne Pictures; **Cover pictures:** *top:* Fritz Prenzel/Bruce Coleman Limited; *bottom:* David Hughes/Bruce Coleman Limited; *globe motif:* Terra Forma™ Copyright© 1995–1997 Andromeda Interactive Ltd.

While every effort has been made to trace the copyright holders of illustrations reproduced in this book, the publishers will be pleased to rectify any omissions or inaccuracies.

Set Index